REVISE INTERNATIONAL GCS

Mathematics A

REVISION GUIDE

Series Consultant: Harry Smith

Author: Harry Smith

A note from the publisher

In order to ensure that this resource offers high-quality support for the associated Edexcel qualification, it has been through a review process by the awarding body to confirm that it fully covers the teaching and learning content of the specification or part of a specification at which it is aimed, and demonstrates an appropriate balance between the development of subject skills, knowledge and understanding, in addition to preparation for assessment.

While the publishers have made every attempt to ensure that advice on the qualification and its assessment is accurate, the official specification and associated assessment guidance materials are the only authoritative source of information and should always be referred to for definitive guidance.

Edexcel examiners have not contributed to any sections in this resource relevant to examination papers for which they have responsibility.

No material from an endorsed resource will be used verbatim in any assessment set by Edexcel.

Endorsement of a resource does not mean that the resource is required to achieve this Edexcel qualification, nor does it mean that it is the only suitable material available to support the qualification, and any resource lists produced by the awarding body shall include this and other appropriate resources.

> **For the full range of Pearson revision titles across International GCSE, GCSE, BTEC and AS Level visit:**
> www.pearsonschools.co.uk/revise

ALWAYS LEARNING

PEARSON

Contents

A small bit of small print

Edexcel publishes Sample Assessment Material and the Specification on its website. This is the official content and this book should be used in conjunction with it. The questions in Now try this have been written to help you practise every topic in the book. Remember: the real exam questions may not look like this.

Calculator skills 1

You can use a calculator in both of your International GCSE exams. Make sure you know how to work out percentages quickly using your calculator.

Calculating with fractions

You can enter fractions on your calculator using the ▣ key and the arrows. For example, to work out $\frac{3}{8}$ of 52:

$$\frac{3}{8} \times 52$$

$$\frac{39}{2}$$

If you want to convert an answer on your calculator display from a fraction to a decimal you can use the S⇔D key.

Quick conversions

You can convert between fractions, decimals and percentages quickly using a calculator:

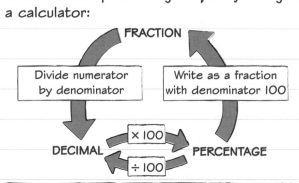

FRACTION

Divide numerator by denominator

Write as a fraction with denominator 100

DECIMAL × 100 PERCENTAGE
         ÷ 100

You can solve lots of percentage problems by working out what 1% represents. To find a percentage of an amount:

> Divide the percentage by 100
>
> Multiply by the amount

Everything in red is part of the answer.

Worked example

A company gives 3.5% of its profits to charity. In 2011 the company made profits of £470 000. How much money did the company give to charity in 2011? **(2 marks)**

$3.5 \div 100 = 0.035$

$0.035 \times 470\,000 = 16\,450$

The company gave £16 450 to charity.

Worked example

In a year group of 85 students, 62 buy their lunch at school. Express 62 as a percentage of 85. Give your answer correct to 1 decimal place. **(2 marks)**

$62 \div 85 = 0.72941...$

$0.72941... \times 100 = 72.941...$

72.9% of students buy their lunch in school.

To write one quantity as a percentage of another:

> Divide the first quantity by the second quantity
>
> Multiply your answer by 100

Always write down at least five digits from your calculator display before rounding your answer.

Now try this

1 Last year a university had 226 graduates. 195 of them found jobs immediately.

   Express 195 as a percentage of 226. Give your answer correct to 1 decimal place. **(2 marks)**

2 Aisha earns $2230 per month and spends 25% of it on rent. Joshua earns $1800 per month and spends 30% on rent.

   Who spends the greater amount on rent? **(3 marks)**

There is more on rounding on page 5.

Factors and primes

The FACTORS of a number are any numbers that divide into it exactly.

A PRIME NUMBER has exactly two factors. It can only be divided by 1 and itself.

Prime factors

If a number is a factor of another number AND it is a prime number then it is called a PRIME FACTOR. You use a factor tree to find prime factors.

Remember to circle the prime factors as you go along. The order doesn't matter.

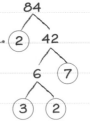

$84 = 2 \times 2 \times 3 \times 7$ ⟶ Remember to put in the multiplication signs.

$= 2^2 \times 3 \times 7$ ⟶ This is called a PRODUCT of PRIME FACTORS.

The highest common factor (HCF) of two numbers is the HIGHEST NUMBER that is a FACTOR of both numbers.

The lowest common multiple (LCM) of two numbers is the LOWEST NUMBER that is a MULTIPLE of both numbers.

Worked example

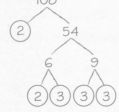

(a) Write 108 as the product of its prime factors. Give your answer in index form. **(3 marks)**

$108 = 2 \times 2 \times 3 \times 3 \times 3 = 2^2 \times 3^3$

(b) Work out the highest common factor (HCF) of 108 and 24. **(2 marks)**

$108 = ②\times②\times③\times 3 \times 3$
$24 = ②\times②\times 2 \times③$
HCF is $2 \times 2 \times 3 = 12$

(c) Work out the lowest common multiple (LCM) of 108 and 24. **(2 marks)**

$LCM = 12 \times 3 \times 3 \times 2 = 216$

Draw a factor tree. Continue until every branch ends with a prime number. This question asks you to write your answer in **index form**. This means you need to use **powers** to say how many times each prime number occurs in the product.

Check it!

$2^2 \times 3^3 = 4 \times 27 = 108$ ✓

To find the HCF circle all the prime numbers which are **common** to both products of prime factors. 2 appears twice in both products so you have to circle it twice. Multiply the circled numbers together to find the HCF.

To find the LCM multiply the HCF by the numbers in both products that were not circled in part **(b)**. You could also multiply 108 and 24 together and divide by the HCF:

$108 \times 24 = 2592$

$2592 \div 12 = 216$

Now try this

1 (a) Express 980 as a product of its prime factors. **(3 marks)**

(b) Find the Highest Common Factor (HCF) of 980 and 56. **(2 marks)**

2 $X = 2 \times 3^5 \times 7^2$
$Y = 3^2 \times 5 \times 7$

Find the Highest Common Factor (HCF) of X and Y. **(2 marks)**

Indices 1

The index laws tell you how to work with POWERS of numbers.

 1 Index laws

Indices include square roots, cube roots and powers.

You can use the index laws to simplify powers and roots.

$a^m \times a^n = a^{m+n}$

$4^3 \times 4^7 = 4^{3+7} = 4^{10}$

$\dfrac{a^m}{a^n} = a^{m-n}$

$12^8 \div 12^3 = 12^{8-3} = 12^5$

$(a^m)^n = a^{mn}$

$(7^3)^5 = 7^{3 \times 5} = 7^{15}$

 2 Cube root

The cube root of a positive number is positive.

$4 \times 4 \times 4 = 64$

$4^3 = 64$

$\sqrt[3]{64} = 4$

The cube root of a negative number is negative.

$-4 \times -4 \times -4 = -64$

$(-4)^3 = -64$

$\sqrt[3]{-64} = -4$

3 Powers of 0 and 1

Anything raised to the power 0 is equal to 1.

$6^0 = 1$ $1^0 = 1$ $7223^0 = 1$ $(-5)^0 = 1$

Anything raised to the power 1 is equal to itself.

$8^1 = 8$ $499^1 = 499$ $(-3)^1 = -3$

Indices checklist

The base numbers have to be the same.

If there's no index, the number has the power 1

Be careful with negatives: $(-3)^2 = 9$

Worked example

(a) Write $6 \times 6 \times 6 \times 6 \times 6$ as a single power of 6. **(1 mark)**

$6 \times 6 \times 6 \times 6 \times 6 = 6^5$

(b) Simplify $\dfrac{3^8 \times 3}{3^4}$ fully, leaving your answer in index form. **(2 marks)**

$\dfrac{3^8 \times 3}{3^4} = \dfrac{3^9}{3^4} = 3^5$

3 is the same as 3^1. For part (b), use the rule $a^m \times a^n = a^{m+n}$ to simplify the numerator, then use $\dfrac{a^m}{a^n} = a^{m-n}$ to simplify the fraction. Remember to write down both steps of your working and give your answer as a power.

Learn it!

You need to be able to recognise the square numbers up to 15^2 and the cubes of 1, 2, 3, 4, 5 and 10. You can check with a calculator but you'll be more confident if you learn them.

For 1(b), start by working out $\dfrac{9625}{7 \times 11}$

Now try this

1 (a) Write $7^3 \times 7^5$ as a single power of 7. **(1 mark)**

(b) $9625 = 5^n \times 7 \times 11$

   Find the value of n. **(2 marks)**

2 $\left(\sqrt[3]{-27}\right)^k = 9$

   Write down the value of k. **(2 marks)**

3 (a) Simplify, leaving your answers in index form

   (i) $\dfrac{2^9}{2^5}$ (ii) $(7^2)^6$ (iii) $5^2 \times 5^0$ **(3 marks)**

(b) $\dfrac{3^n}{3^2 \times 3^5} = 3^4$

   Find the value of n. **(2 marks)**

Indices 2

You can use these index laws to deal with powers that are FRACTIONS or NEGATIVE NUMBERS.

 Negative powers

$$a^{-n} = \frac{1}{a^n}$$

$$5^{-2} = \frac{1}{5^2} = \frac{1}{25}$$

Be careful!

A NEGATIVE power can still have a POSITIVE answer.

 Reciprocals

$$a^{-1} = \frac{1}{a}$$

This means that a^{-1} is the RECIPROCAL of a. You can find the reciprocal of a fraction by turning it upside down.

$$\left(\frac{5}{9}\right)^{-1} = \frac{9}{5}$$

3 Powers of fractions

$$\left(\frac{a}{b}\right)^n = \frac{a^n}{b^n}$$

$$\left(\frac{3}{10}\right)^2 = \frac{3^2}{10^2} = \frac{9}{100}$$

4 Combining rules

You can apply the rules one at a time.

$$\left(\frac{a}{b}\right)^{-n} = \left(\frac{b}{a}\right)^n = \frac{b^n}{a^n}$$

$$\left(\frac{2}{3}\right)^{-3} = \left(\frac{3}{2}\right)^3 = \frac{3^3}{2^3} = \frac{27}{8}$$

5 Fractional powers

You can use fractional powers to represent roots.

$$a^{\frac{1}{2}} = \sqrt{a} \qquad 49^{\frac{1}{2}} = \pm 7$$

$$a^{\frac{1}{3}} = \sqrt[3]{a} \qquad 27^{\frac{1}{3}} = 3$$

$$a^{\frac{1}{4}} = \sqrt[4]{a} \qquad 16^{\frac{1}{4}} = \pm 2$$

Check it!

A whole number raised to a power less than 1 gets smaller.

6 More complicated indices

You can use the index laws to work out more complicated fractional powers.

$$a^{\frac{m}{n}} = \left(a^{\frac{1}{n}}\right)^m$$

Do these calculations ONE STEP AT A TIME.

$$27^{-\frac{2}{3}} = (27^{\frac{1}{3}})^{-2}$$

$$= (\sqrt[3]{27})^{-2}$$

$$= 3^{-2} = \frac{1}{3^2} = \frac{1}{9}$$

Worked example

Find the value of n when $3^n = 9^{-\frac{3}{2}}$
Show each step of your working clearly. **(3 marks)**

$$9^{-\frac{3}{2}} = (3^2)^{-\frac{3}{2}}$$

$$= 3^{2 \times -\frac{3}{2}} = 3^{-3}$$

So $3^n = 3^{-3}$ and $n = -3$

3^n is not the same as $3n$. You can't divide by 3 to get n on its own. You need to make the base on the right-hand side the same as the base on the left-hand side.

1. Write 9 as a power of 3. Remember to use brackets.
2. Use $(a^n)^m = a^{nm}$ to write the right-hand side as a single power of 3.
3. Compare both sides and write down the value of n.

Now try this

1 You are given that $x = 7^h$ and $y = 7^k$

Write each of the following as a single power of 7.

(a) $\frac{x}{y}$ **(1 mark)**

(b) x^2 **(1 mark)**

(c) xy^2 **(2 marks)**

 Aiming higher

 Aiming higher

2 Given that $81^{-\frac{3}{4}} = 3^n$, find the value of n. **(3 marks)**

3 Write $\sqrt{\frac{49}{7^3}}$ as a single power of 7. Show every step of your working clearly. **(3 marks)**

Start by writing 49 as a power of 7

Calculator skills 2

These calculator keys are really useful.

x^2	Square a number.	$(-)$	Enter a negative number.
x^3	Cube a number.	$\sqrt{\square}$	Find the square root of a number.
x^{-1}	Find the reciprocal of a number.	$\sqrt[3]{\square}$	Find the cube root of a number. You might need to press the shift key first.
Ans	Use your previous answer in a calculation.	S⇔D	Change the answer from a fraction or surd to a decimal. Not all calculators have this key.

Rounding rules

1 To ROUND a number, you look at the next digit on the right.

5 or more → round up   less than 5 → round down

2 Decimals can be rounded to a given number of DECIMAL PLACES (d.p.).

6.475 = 6.48 correct to 2 d.p.

3 To write a number correct to 3 SIGNIFICANT FIGURES (3 s.f.), look at the fourth significant figure.

0.003 07<u>9</u> = 0.003 08 to 3 s.f.

4 Leading zeros in decimals are not counted as significant.

5 Remember that the rule for significant figures still applies to WHOLE NUMBERS.

27 = 30 to 1 s.f.

Worked example

(a) Work out the value of $\dfrac{\sqrt{8.3}}{12.5 - 7.3}$

Give your answer as a decimal.

Write down all the figures on your calculator display. **(2 marks)**

$$\frac{\sqrt{8.3}}{12.5 - 7.3} = \frac{2.88097}{5.2} = 0.554033088$$

(b) Give your answer to part (a) correct to 2 significant figures. **(1 mark)**

0.55 (2 s.f.)

Calculate $\sqrt{8.3}$ using the $\sqrt{\square}$ key. Always show what the top of the fraction comes to as well as the bottom. Remember to write down **all** the figures on your calculator display.

Check it!

Do the whole calculation in one go on your calculator using the 🔲 key.

Now try this

(a) Work out the value of $\dfrac{6.1 + 7.5}{1.8^2}$

Give your answer as a decimal.

Write down all the figures on your calculator display. **(2 marks)**

(b) Give your answer to part (a) correct to 3 significant figures. **(1 mark)**

Make sure you write down three significant figures even if the last digit is a zero.

5

Fractions

You need to be able to show all your working when calculating with fractions and mixed numbers.

1 Adding or subtracting fractions

| Add or subtract the whole numbers |

$2\frac{2}{3} + 1\frac{1}{2}$

| Write the fractions as fractions with the same denominator |

$= 3 + \frac{2}{3} + \frac{1}{2}$

$= 3 + \frac{4}{6} + \frac{3}{6}$

| Add or subtract the fractions |

$= 3 + \frac{7}{6}$

$= 3 + 1\frac{1}{6}$

| If you have an improper fraction then convert to a mixed number and add |

$= 4\frac{1}{6}$

2 Multiplying fractions

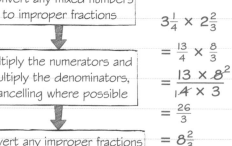

| Convert any mixed numbers to improper fractions |

$3\frac{1}{4} \times 2\frac{2}{3}$

| Multiply the numerators and multiply the denominators, cancelling where possible |

$= \frac{13}{4} \times \frac{8}{3}$

$= \frac{13 \times 8^2}{\cancel{4} \times 3}$

$= \frac{26}{3}$

| Convert any improper fractions to mixed numbers |

$= 8\frac{2}{3}$

3 Dividing fractions

| Convert any mixed numbers to improper fractions |

$6\frac{1}{4} \div 1\frac{7}{8}$

| Turn the second fraction 'upside down' and change ÷ to × |

$= \frac{25}{4} \times \frac{15}{8}$

$= \frac{^5 25 \times 8^2}{_1 4 \times 15_3}$

| Multiply the numerators and multiply the denominators, cancelling where possible |

$= \frac{10}{3}$

$= 3\frac{1}{3}$

| Convert any improper fractions to mixed numbers |

Show that...

In your International GCSE exam, a calculation involving fractions or mixed numbers might say "Show that...". This means you have to:

✓ Start by writing down the left-hand-side of the calculation

✓ Show every step of your working clearly

✓ Finish by writing down the answer

Worked example

Show that $7\frac{1}{3} - 2\frac{3}{4} = 4\frac{7}{12}$ **(3 marks)**

$7\frac{1}{3} - 2\frac{3}{4} = \frac{22}{3} - \frac{11}{4}$

$= \frac{88}{12} - \frac{33}{12}$

$= \frac{55}{12}$

$= 4\frac{7}{12}$

EXAM ALERT!

It's tricky to subtract the whole number parts and fractions separately because $\frac{1}{3} - \frac{3}{4}$ is **negative**. For this question it's safer to convert both mixed numbers to improper fractions first.

Students have struggled with exam questions similar to this – **be prepared!**

Now try this

1 (a) Show that $\frac{7}{10} - \frac{1}{4} = \frac{9}{20}$ **(2 marks)**

(b) Show that $3\frac{4}{9} + 1\frac{5}{6} = 5\frac{5}{18}$ **(3 marks)**

2 (a) Show that $\frac{3}{4} \div \frac{5}{12} = 1\frac{4}{5}$ **(2 marks)**

(b) Show that $1\frac{7}{8} \times 2\frac{2}{3} = 5$ **(3 marks)**

Standard form

Numbers in standard form have two parts.

$$7.3 \times 10^{-6}$$

This part is a number greater than or equal to 1 and less than 10

This part is a power of 10

You can use standard form to write very large or very small numbers.

$$920\,000 = 9.2 \times 10^5$$

Numbers greater than 10 have a positive power of 10

$$0.007\,03 = 7.03 \times 10^{-3}$$

Numbers less than 1 have a negative power of 10

Counting decimal places

You can count decimal places to convert between numbers in standard form and ordinary numbers.

3 jumps

$$7\,9\,0\,0 = 7.9 \times 10^3$$

| $7900 > 10$ So the power is positive |

4 jumps

$$0.0\,0\,0\,3\,5 = 3.5 \times 10^{-4}$$

| $0.00035 < 1$ So the power is negative |

BE CAREFUL!
Don't just count zeros to work out the power.

Worked example

(a) Write 1 630 000 in standard form.   **(1 mark)**

1.63×10^6

(b) Write 4.2×10^{-3} as an ordinary number.   **(1 mark)**

0.0042

Count the number of decimal places you need to move to get a number between 1 and 10. 1 630 000 is bigger than 10 so the power will be positive.

Using a calculator

You can enter numbers in standard form using the $\boxed{\times 10^x}$ key.

To enter 3.7×10^{-6} press

$\boxed{3}\ \boxed{.}\ \boxed{7}\ \boxed{\times 10^x}\ \boxed{(-)}\ \boxed{6}$

If you are using a calculator with numbers in standard form it is a good idea to put brackets around each number.

For part (b) you would enter:

$\boxed{(}\ \boxed{1}\ \boxed{.}\ \boxed{9}\ \boxed{\times 10^x}\ \boxed{4}\ \boxed{)}\ \boxed{x^2}\ \boxed{=}$

Worked example

Aiming higher

A and B are standard form numbers.

$A = 1.9 \times 10^4 \quad B = 4.2 \times 10^5$

Calculate, giving your answers in standard form:

(a) $A + B$ **(1 mark)**

$(1.9 \times 10^4) + (4.2 \times 10^5) = 439\,000$
$\qquad\qquad\qquad\qquad\quad = 4.39 \times 10^5$

(b) A^2 **(1 mark)**

$(1.9 \times 10^4)^2 = 3.61 \times 10^8$

Now try this

The mass of an empty Airbus A380 is 2.77×10^5 kg.

(a) Write 2.77×10^5 as an ordinary number.   **(1 mark)**

On take off, an A380 carries 2.4×10^5 kg of fuel and passengers and crew with a total mass of 3.41×10^4 kg.

(b) Calculate the total take off weight of the A380. Give your answer in standard form.   **(2 marks)**

Percentage change

There are two methods that can be used to increase or decrease an amount by a percentage.

Method 1

Work out 26% of £280:

$\frac{26}{100}$ × £280 = £72.80

Subtract the decrease:

£280 − £72.80 = £207.20

£280

26% OFF

Method 2

Use a multiplier:

100% + 30% = 130%

$\frac{130}{100}$ = 1.3

So the multiplier for a 30% increase is 1.3:

400 g × 1.3 = 520 g

400 g
PLUS
30% EXTRA

Worked example

A football club increases the prices of its season tickets by 5.2% each year.

In 2011 a top-price season ticket cost £650.

Calculate the price of this season ticket in 2012.   **(3 marks)**

$\frac{5.2}{100}$ × £650 = £33.80

£650 + £33.80 = £683.80

When working with money, you must give your answer to 2 decimal places.

Check it!

Choose an easy percentage which is close to 5.2%

10% of £650 is £65, so 5% is £32.50

£650 + £32.50 = £682.50, which is close to £683.80 ✓

Calculating a percentage increase or decrease

Work out the amount of the increase or decrease

⬇

Write this as a percentage of the original amount

Was £60
Now £39

60 − 39 = 21

$\frac{21}{60}$ = 35%

This is a 35% decrease.

A question may ask you to calculate a percentage **profit** or **loss** rather than an increase or decrease.

For a reminder about writing one quantity as a percentage of another, have a look at page 1.

Now try this

1 A car manufacturer increases its prices by 8%.
The price of a particular model before the increase was £13 250.
What will this particular model cost after the price increase?   **(3 marks)**

2 A TV originally cost £520.
In a sale it was priced at £340.
What was the percentage reduction in the price? Give your answer to 1 decimal place.   **(3 marks)**

Reduction means decrease. Work out the decrease as a percentage of the original price.

Reverse percentages and compound interest

Reverse percentages

In some questions you are given an amount AFTER a percentage change.

To find the original amount you divide by the MULTIPLIER.

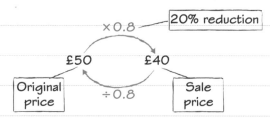

×0.8 — 20% reduction

£50 → £40

Original price   ÷0.8   Sale price

Worked example

In a sale, normal prices are reduced by 15%

The sale price of a pair of trainers is £75.65

Work out the normal price of the trainers.

(3 marks)

$100\% - 15\% = 85\%$

$\dfrac{85}{100} = 0.85$

$75.65 \div 0.85 = 89$

The original price was £89

EXAM ALERT!

Do **not** increase the price given by 15%

Subtract to find the multiplier for a 15% decrease then **divide** the new amount by the multiplier.

Check it!
Reduce £89 by 15%:
£89 × 0.85 = £75.65 ✓

Students have struggled with exam questions similar to this – **be prepared!**

Compound interest

If you leave your money in a bank account it will earn compound interest.

This table shows the total interest earned after 3 years at 3% compound interest.

Year	Balance (£)	Interest earned (£)
1	40 000	1200
2	41 200	1236
3	42 436	1273.08
	43 709.08	3709.08

For year 2 you have to calculate 3% of £41 200

After 3 years the total interest earned will be £3709.08 and the balance will be £43 709.08

Repeated change

Compound interest is an example of REPEATED PERCENTAGE CHANGE. You can use multipliers to calculate repeated percentage changes quickly.

This car DEPRECIATES in value by 8% each year.

£15 000

The multiplier for an 8% decrease is 0.92

After 3 years the car is worth:

£15 000 × 0.92 × 0.92 × 0.92
= £15 000 × 0.92^3 = £11 680.32

Now try this

The multiplier for a 2% increase is 1.02

1 Hannah buys some shoes in a sale where all the items are marked '40% off'.
   She pays £27 for the shoes.
   What price were the shoes originally?
   (3 marks)

2 The population of a city is 183 000.
   The population is increasing at the rate of 2% per year.
   Estimate the population in 5 years' time. Give your answer to 3 significant figures. **(3 marks)**

Recurring decimals

Some fractions convert into RECURRING decimals. A recurring decimal has a digit or a group of digits that repeats forever. You can use dots to show the recurring digits.

$\frac{2}{3} = 0.66666... = 0.\dot{6}$ ——— The dot over the 6 tells you that this digit repeats forever.

$\frac{346}{555} = 0.6234234... = 0.6\dot{2}3\dot{4}$ ——— The dots tell you that the group of digits 234 repeats forever.

Worked example

Aiming higher

Show that the recurring decimal
$0.\dot{2}\dot{4} = \frac{8}{33}$ **(2 marks)**

Let $n =$ 0.242 424 24...

$100n =$ 24.242 424 24...

$- n =$ 0.242 424 24...

_____

$99n = 24$

$n = \frac{24}{99} = \frac{8}{33}$

Some calculators will convert recurring decimals into fractions for you. But the question says "Show that..." so you must write down all the steps shown here.

1. Write the recurring decimal equal to n, and write out some of its digits.

2. Multiply both sides by 100 as there are 2 recurring digits.

3. Subtract n to remove the recurring part.

4. Divide both sides by 99 to write n as a fraction.

5. Simplify the fraction.

Multiply by...

10 if 1 digit recurs. ✓

100 if 2 digits recur. ✓

1000 if 3 digits recur. ✓

In this recurring decimal the digit 4 does not recur. Follow the same steps to write n as a fraction. After you divide by 99, multiply the top and bottom of your fraction by 10 to convert the decimal in the numerator into an integer.

Worked example

Aiming higher

Show that $0.4\dot{7}\dot{3}$ can be written as the fraction $\frac{469}{990}$ **(2 marks)**

Let $n =$ 0.473 737 37...

$100n =$ 47.373 737 37...

$- n =$ 0.473 737 37...

_____

$99n = 46.9$

$n = \frac{46.9}{99}$

$n = \frac{469}{990}$

Now try this

1 Show that the recurring decimal
   $0.0\dot{1}\dot{8} = \frac{1}{55}$ **(2 marks)**

2 Show that the recurring decimal
   $0.\dot{3}5\dot{1} = \frac{13}{37}$ **(2 marks)**

$0.\dot{3}5\dot{1} = 0.351351351...$

There are 3 recurring digits so you need to write $0.\dot{3}5\dot{1}$ as n, then multiply by 1000. You will get a fraction with denominator 999 which you can simplify.

Ratio

RATIOS are used to compare quantities. You can find equivalent ratios by multiplying or dividing by the same number.

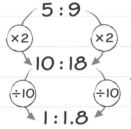

This equivalent ratio is in the form 1 : *n*. This is useful for calculations.

Simplest form

To write a ratio in its simplest form, find an equivalent ratio with the smallest possible whole number values.

Simplest form
5 : 1   10 : 9
2 : 3 : 4

NOT simplest form
10 : 2   1 : 0.9
1 : 1.5 : 2

Worked example

Alexis and Nisha share a flat. They decide to split their phone bill in the ratio 3 : 5

Alexis pays £78. How much does Nisha pay?   **(2 marks)**

78 ÷ 3 = 26

26 × 5 = 130

Nisha pays £130

Work out the value of one part of the ratio first. You could also use equivalent ratios to solve this problem. Work out how many 3s go into 78 to find the multiplier.

Check it!
£130 + £78 = £208
Divide £208 in the ratio 3 : 5
3 + 5 = 8 parts in the ratio in total
£208 ÷ 8 = £26
£26 × 3 = £78 ✓

Worked example

A university course has 945 applicants for 126 places.

(a) Find the ratio of the number of applicants to the number of places. Give your ratio in the form *n* : 1   **(2 marks)**

945 ÷ 126 = 7.5

Applicants : Places = 945 : 126
                    = 7.5 : 1

(b) Of the 126 successful applicants, the ratio of males to females is 4 : 5

Work out the number of females on the course.   **(2 marks)**

4 + 5 = 9
126 ÷ 9 = 14
14 × 5 = 70

There were 70 females on the course.

Work out the total number of parts in the ratio, then divide 126 by this to work out how many people each part represents. Then multiply by 5 to work out the number of females.

Now try this

1 Andre, Becky and Chrissie share some money in the ratios 3 : 6 : 7. In total Andre and Becky receive $207.

Work out the amount of money Chrissie receives.   **(2 marks)**

2 The ratio of Amir's age to Petra's age is 3 : 7
Amir is 9 years old.
(a) Work out Petra's age.   **(2 marks)**

The ratio of Karl's age to Yasmina's age is 5 : 2
The sum of their ages is 84.
(b) Work out Yasmina's age.   **(2 marks)**

Proportion

Two quantities are in DIRECT PROPORTION when both quantities increase at the same rate.

Number of theatre tickets bought   Total cost

3

£135

×3   ×3

9   £405

Two quantities are in INVERSE PROPORTION when one quantity increases at the same rate as the other quantity decreases.

Average speed   Time taken

40 km/h

2 hours

×2   ÷2

80 km/h   1 hour

Worked example

Here are the ingredients for apple crumble.

Apple crumble
Serves 6 people
900 g apples
180 g sugar
90 g butter
150 g flour

(a) Henry wants to make apple crumble for 11 people. Work out the amount of sugar he needs. **(2 marks)**

Amount needed for 1 person = $\frac{180}{6}$ = 30 g

Amount needed for 11 people = 11 × 30 = 330 g

(b) Carla makes an apple crumble using 2250 g of apples. Work out how many people her apple crumble will serve. **(2 marks)**

2250 ÷ 900 = 2.5
6 × 2.5 = 15
The apple crumble will serve 15 people.

Divide or multiply?

You can use common sense to work out whether to divide or multiply in proportion questions.

6 people can build a wall in 4 days.

6 × 4 = 24 so 1 person could build the wall in 24 days.

MULTIPLY because it would take 1 person LONGER to build the wall.

24 ÷ 8 = 3 so 8 people could build the wall in 3 days.

DIVIDE because it would take 8 people LESS TIME to build the wall.

There were 365 days in 2010 in total. So you can **estimate** that $\frac{1}{365}$ of the spectators had a birthday on that day. You can only have a whole number of people so make sure you round your answer to the nearest whole number. There are other estimates that are valid as well, but make sure you show all your working.

Worked example

There were 84 890 spectators at the World Cup Final in South Africa on 11 July, 2010.

Work out an estimate for the number of those spectators whose birthday was on that day. **(4 marks)**

84 890 × $\frac{1}{365}$ = 232.57534...

Approximately 233 people had a birthday on that day.

Now try this

Here are the ingredients for 12 meringues.

Meringues
To make 12 meringues:
3 egg whites   165 g caster sugar

(a) Makito wants to make 20 meringues. Work out the amount of sugar he needs. **(2 marks)**

(b) Ethan has 5 eggs. Work out how many meringues he can make if he uses them all. **(2 marks)**

Upper and lower bounds

Upper and lower bounds are a measure of accuracy. For example, the width of a postcard is given as 8 cm to the nearest cm.

The actual width of the postcard could be anything between 7.5 cm and 8.5 cm.

7.5 cm is called the LOWER BOUND.

8.5 cm is called the UPPER BOUND.

```
        lower            upper
        bound            bound
      ├─────┼──────┼──────┼─────┤
    7 cm  7.5 cm  8 cm  8.5 cm  9 cm
            ←──────────────→
```

Using upper and lower bounds in calculations

To find the overall upper and lower bounds of the answer to a calculation use these rules.

	+	−	×	÷
Overall upper bound	UB + UB	UB − LB	UB × UB	UB ÷ LB
Overall lower bound	LB + LB	LB − UB	LB × LB	LB ÷ UB

Overall lower bound of $a + b$ = lower bound of a + lower bound of b

---

Worked example

A roll of ribbon is 100 cm long, correct to 2 significant figures.

A 21 cm piece of ribbon is cut off the roll, correct to the nearest cm.

Calculate the lower bound, in cm, for the amount of ribbon remaining on the roll. **(3 mark)**

	Lower bound	Upper bound
Length of ribbon	95 cm	105 cm
Length of piece cut off	20.5 cm	21.5 cm

Lower bound of remaining length
= 95 − 21.5
= 73.5 cm

If you're answering questions about upper and lower bounds, it's a good idea to write out the upper bound and lower bound for **all values** given in the question before you start. To work out the **lower bound** for $a - b$ you need to use the **lower bound** for a and the **upper bound** for b.

EXAM ALERT!

Different values might be given to **different degrees of accuracy**. The length of the roll is correct to 2 significant figures, or to the nearest **10 cm**. The length of the piece cut off is correct to the nearest **cm**. Be really careful when you're working out your upper and lower bounds.

Students have struggled with exam questions similar to this – **be prepared!**

Now try this

1 The area of a rectangle is 320 cm². The length of the rectangle is 22 cm. Both values are correct to 2 significant figures. Calculate the lower bound for the width of the rectangle. Show your working clearly.

(3 marks)

2 Correct to 2 decimal places, the volume of a solid cube is 3.37 m³. Calculate the upper bound for the surface area of the cube. **(4 marks)**

For a cube with edges of length x, the volume is x^3 and the surface area is $6x^2$

13

Surds 1

You can give exact answers to calculations by leaving some numbers as square roots.

? | Area = 10 cm²

This square has a side length of $\sqrt{10}$ cm.

You can't write $\sqrt{10}$ exactly as a decimal number. It is called a SURD.

Rules for simplifying square roots

These are the most important rules to remember when dealing with surds.

$$\sqrt{ab} = \sqrt{a} \times \sqrt{b}$$

$$\sqrt{8} = \sqrt{4} \times \sqrt{2} = 2\sqrt{2}$$

$$\sqrt{\frac{a}{b}} = \frac{\sqrt{a}}{\sqrt{b}}$$ $$\sqrt{\frac{3}{25}} = \frac{\sqrt{3}}{\sqrt{25}} = \frac{\sqrt{3}}{5}$$

You need to remember these rules for your exam. They are NOT given on the formula sheet.

Worked example

Aiming higher

Show that $\sqrt{45} = 3\sqrt{5}$
Show each stage of your working clearly.
(2 marks)

$$\sqrt{45} = \sqrt{9 \times 5}$$
$$= \sqrt{9} \times \sqrt{5}$$
$$= 3\sqrt{5}$$

This question says "Show that..." so you can't use your calculator. You need to show each step of your working clearly:

1. Look for a factor of 45 which is a square number: $45 = 9 \times 5$

2. Use the rule $\sqrt{ab} = \sqrt{a} \times \sqrt{b}$ to split the square root into two square roots.

3. Write $\sqrt{9}$ as a whole number.

RATIONALISING THE DENOMINATOR of a fraction means making the denominator a whole number.

You can do this by multiplying the top AND bottom of the fraction by the surd part in the denominator.

$$\frac{5}{3\sqrt{2}} = \frac{5\sqrt{2}}{6}$$

×$\sqrt{2}$ (top and bottom)

The surd part of the denominator is $\sqrt{2}$

Remember that $\sqrt{2} \times \sqrt{2} = 2$
So $3\sqrt{2} \times \sqrt{2} = 3 \times 2 = 6$

Good form

Most surd questions ask you to write a number or answer in a certain FORM.

This means you need to find INTEGERS for all the letters in the expression.

$6\sqrt{3}$ is in the form $k\sqrt{3}$

$$k = 6$$

The integers can be positive or negative.

$4 - 9\sqrt{2}$ is in the form $p + q\sqrt{2}$

$$p = 4 \text{ and } q = -9$$

You can check your answer by writing down the integer value for each letter.

Now try this

Find factors of 32 and 98 which are **square** numbers.

1 Write $\sqrt{32} + \sqrt{98}$ in the form $p\sqrt{2}$ where p is an integer. Show each stage of your working clearly. **(2 marks)**

2 Show that $\frac{35}{\sqrt{7}} = 5\sqrt{7}$ **(2 marks)**

Rationalise the denominator by multiplying top and bottom by $\sqrt{7}$

3 x is an integer such that $\frac{\sqrt{x} \times \sqrt{18}}{\sqrt{3}} = 8\sqrt{3}$
Find the value of x. **(4 marks)**

Set notation

In mathematics a SET is a collection of ELEMENTS (or MEMBERS). The elements in a set could be numbers, words or letters. You can define a set in TWO different ways:

 Listing the elements

A = {onions, carrots, peas} → You use curly brackets to define a set.

B = {13, 14, 15, 16} → Elements are separated by commas.

→ This set contains 4 elements. You write n(B) = 4

 Using a rule

JUNE is a member of this set.

C = {months with exactly 30 days} → You can write JUNE ∈ C. The symbol ∈ means "is a member of".

D = {odd numbers between 10 and 20}

→ You could also write set D as {11, 13, 15, 17, 19}. It has 5 members so you write n(D) = 5

Union and intersection

U means UNION. The union of two sets is the set of elements that belong to EITHER set.

∩ means INTERSECTION. The intersection of two sets is the set of elements that belong to BOTH sets.

All or nothing

The symbol ℰ represents the UNIVERSAL SET. This is the set of all the elements that you are allowed to consider in a particular question.

The symbol Ø is used to represent the EMPTY set. It contains NO ELEMENTS.

Worked example

A = {d, a, v, i, d}
B = {g, o, l, i, a, t, h}
List the members of the set

(a) A ∩ B   **(1 mark)**

A ∩ B = {i, a}

(b) A ∪ B   **(1 mark)**

A ∪ B = {d, a, v, i, d, g, o, l, t, h}

EXAM ALERT!

In part (b) you need to write the **union** of sets A and B. Make sure that you only include each element **once**, even if it appears in both sets.

Students have struggled with exam questions similar to this – **be prepared!**

Worked example

ℰ = {positive whole numbers **less than** 15}
X = {multiples of 5}
Y = {multiples of 3}

(a) Is it true that 20 ∈ X? Explain your answer.   **(1 mark)**

No. The universal set is numbers less than 15, so 20 cannot be a member of any set.

(b) Is it true that X ∩ Y = Ø? Explain your answer.   **(1 mark)**

Yes. X = {5, 10} and Y = {3, 6, 9, 12}. These sets have no common members, so their union is the empty set.

Now try this

 Aiming higher

1 P = {m, e, t, r, i, c}
Q = {i, g, c, s, e}
List the members of the set
(a) P ∩ Q   **(1 mark)**
(b) P ∪ Q   **(1 mark)**

2 A = {factors of 20}   B = {prime numbers}
(a) Is it true that A ∩ B = Ø? Explain your answer.   **(1 mark)**
(b) Work out n(A ∩ B)   **(1 mark)**

 n(A ∩ B) means the number of elements in A ∩ B

Venn diagrams

You can represent two or more sets on a VENN DIAGRAM.
This Venn diagram shows two sets A and B:

The UNIVERSAL set ($\mathcal{E}$) is drawn as a rectangle around the other sets.

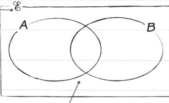

This shaded area represents A ∩ B

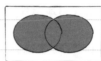

This shaded area represents A ∪ B
There is more on INTERSECTION and UNION on page 15.

You draw each set as a circle. If the circles overlap than the sets INTERSECT.

Complements of sets

The complement of a set P is written as P'. You say 'not P' or 'the complement of P'.

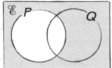

The shaded area represents P'.

Subsets

If X is a subset of Y it is COMPLETELY CONTAINED inside Y. You write X ⊂ Y

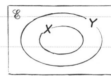

Every member of X is also a member of Y.

Worked example

A, B and C are sets, with B ∩ C = ∅ and A ⊂ B

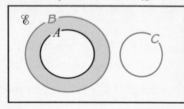

(a) Complete the Venn diagram to show sets B and C. **(2 marks)**

(b) On the Venn diagram, shade the region that represents B ∩ A' **(1 mark)**

Worked example

This Venn diagram shows three sets.

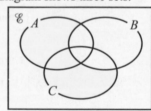

Use set notation to describe the shaded region. **(2 marks)**

(A ∪ C) ∩ B'

This means 'A or C and not B'.

Now try this

On separate copies of this Venn diagram, shade the region represented by:

(a) P ∪ Q **(1 mark)**

(b) Q' **(1 mark)**

(c) R ∩ P' **(1 mark)**

(d) P ∪ (Q ∩ R) **(1 mark)**

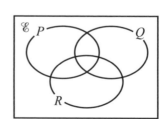

Problem-solving with sets

You can write NUMBERS in the sections of a Venn diagram to show the NUMBER OF ELEMENTS (or MEMBERS) that are contained in that section. This Venn diagram shows whether a group of 50 people own a dog, a cat or both.

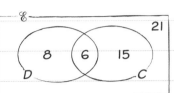

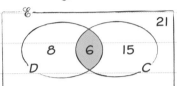

6 people owned a dog AND a cat. You can write

$n(D \cap C) = 6$

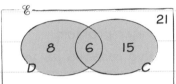

$8 + 6 + 15 = 29$ people in total owned a dog OR a cat. You can write $n(D \cup C) = 29$

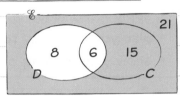

$15 + 21 = 36$ people DID NOT own a dog. You can write $n(D') = 36$

Worked example
Aiming higher

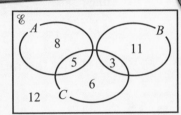

Find

(a) $n(B \cup C)$ **(1 mark)**

$n(B \cup C) = 5 + 6 + 3 + 11 = 25$

(b) $n(C')$ **(1 mark)**

$n(C') = 12 + 8 + 11 = 31$

(c) $n(B' \cap C')$ **(1 mark)**

$n(B' \cap C') = 12 + 8 = 20$

It is helpful to draw three sketches of the Venn diagram and shade in the relevant sections:

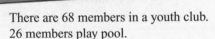

$B \cup C$ C' $B' \cap C'$

For parts (b) and (c), make sure you include the 12 elements that are in the **universal set** but are not in any of the other sets.

EXAM ALERT!

The safest way to answer this question is by drawing a Venn diagram. You don't know the number of people who play pool and table-tennis, $n(P \cap T)$, so write it as x. You know that $n(P) = 26$, so you can write $n(P \cap T')$ as $26 - x$. Use the fact that $n(\mathscr{E}) = 68$ to write an equation and solve it to find x.

Students have struggled with exam questions similar to this – **be prepared!**

Worked example
Aiming higher

There are 68 members in a youth club.
26 members play pool.
35 members play table-tennis.
14 members do not play pool or table-tennis.
Find the number of members that play both pool and table-tennis. **(3 marks)**

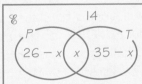

$14 + (26 - x) + x + (35 - x) = 68$
$75 - x = 68$
$x = 7$

7 members play both pool and table-tennis.

Now try this
Aiming higher

An Indian restaurant served 50 tables in one evening.
41 tables ordered naan bread.
18 tables ordered roti bread.
5 tables didn't order either type of bread.

Find the number of tables that ordered naan bread **but not** roti bread. **(3 marks)**

Problem-solving practice

Problem-solving skills are essential to success in your International GCSE exam.

Practise using the questions on the next two pages.

For these questions you might need to:

- choose which mathematical technique or skill to use
- apply a technique in a new context
- plan your strategy to solve a longer problem
- show your working clearly and give reasons for your answers.

1 At a sixth form college, the ratio of male to female students is 7 : 6
There are 144 female students at the college. How many students are there in total?
(2 marks)

Ratio p. 11

Use the information in the question to work out what each part of the ratio represents. There are 7 + 6 = 13 parts in the ratio, so multiply your answer by 13 to work out the total number of students.

TOP TIP

Check your answer by dividing it in the ratio 7 : 6

2 $\mathscr{E}$ = {odd numbers}
X = {1, 3, 5, 7, 9, 11}

(a) Y is a set such that
$X \cap Y$ = {5, 9} n(Y) = 3
List the members of one possible set Y.   (2 marks)

(b) Z is a set such that $X \cap Z$ = Ø
n(Z) = 3
List the members of one possible set Z.   (2 marks)

Set notation p. 15

(a) ∩ means intersection, so the members of $X \cap Y$ must be members of X **and** members of Y. So the elements 5 and 9 must be in your new set Y. Choose any other member of $\mathscr{E}$ that **isn't** a member of X. Remember, n(Y) = 3 means that Y must have three members.

(b) $X \cap Z$ = Ø means that X and Z have no members in common.

TOP TIP

In a sets question, always check the **universal set, $\mathscr{E}$.** You can **only** pick your members from within this set.

3 This item appeared in a newspaper.

> ### Cow produces 3% more milk
> A farmer found that when his cow listened to classical music the milk it produced increased by 3%.
> This increase of 3% represented 0.72 litres of milk.

Calculate the amount of milk produced by the cow when it listened to classical music.   (3 marks)

Proportion p. 12
Percentage change p. 8

When the cow listened to classical music, it produced 103% of the milk it produced originally. You know that 3% represents 0.72 litres. Use this information to work out what 103% represents.

TOP TIP

You can sometimes solve percentage problems by working out what 1% represents.

Problem-solving practice

 4 (a) $a = 4 \times 10^{2n}$ where n is an integer.

Find, in standard form, an expression for $\sqrt{a}$ (2 marks)

(b) $b = 8 \times 10^{3m}$ where m is an integer.

Find, in standard form, an expression for $b^{\frac{4}{3}}$ (3 marks)

Standard form p. 7
Indices 2 p. 4

Remember that $(xy)^n = x^n y^n$

Be careful in part (b): the first part of a number in standard form must be greater than or equal to 1 and less than 10.

TOP TIP

Questions on indices can involve unknowns, so your calculator won't be able to help you. Make sure you know the laws of indices.

---

 5 Aminata invested £2500 for n years in a savings account.

She was paid 3% per annum compound interest.

At the end of n years, Aminata had £2813.77 in the savings account.

Work out the value of n.   (2 marks)

Reverse percentages and compound interest p. 9   *Aiming higher*

You are normally given the number of years for a compound interest question and have to calculate the amount. Here you need to work out the number of years, n. You know that n is going to be a whole number, so work out the totals after 1 year, 2 years, 3 years, etc.

TOP TIP

Read the question carefully and make sure you know what you are being asked to work out.

---

 6 The diagram shows a wooden planting box in the shape of a cuboid.

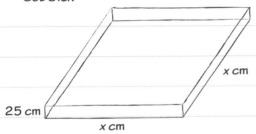

The volume of the box is 810 000 cm³ correct to 2 significant figures.

The depth of the box is 25 cm, to the nearest cm.

The box has a square base with sides of length x cm.

Find the lower bound for x. Give your answer correct to 3 significant figures.   (4 marks)

Upper and lower bounds p.13   *Aiming higher*
Volumes of 3-D shapes p.65

Complete this table showing the upper and lower bounds for each measurement before you start:

	25 cm	810 000 cm
Upper	25.5 cm	
Lower	805 000 cm	

You are **dividing** the volume by the depth to work out x^2. Choose the values you use carefully to make the answer as **small** as possible.

TOP TIP

When answering questions about upper and lower bounds, it's a good idea to write out the upper and lower bounds for all the values before you start.

Algebraic expressions

You need to be able to work with algebraic expressions confidently. For a reminder about using the index laws with NUMBERS have a look at pages 3 and 4.

① You can use the INDEX LAWS to simplify algebraic expressions.

$a^m \times a^n = a^{m+n}$

$x^4 \times x^3 = x^{4+3} = x^7$

$\dfrac{a^m}{a^n} = a^{m-n}$

$m^8 \div m^2 = m^{8-2} = m^6$

$(a^m)^n = a^{mn}$

$(n^2)^4 = n^{2 \times 4} = n^8$

② You can square or cube a whole expression.

$(4x^3y)^2 = (4)^2 \times (x^3)^2 \times (y)^2$
$\qquad\qquad = 16x^6y^2$

You need to square everything inside the brackets.

$16 = (4)^2$

$(x^3)^2 = x^{3 \times 2} = x^6$

Remember that if a letter appears on its own then it has the power 1.

③ Algebraic expressions may also contain negative and fractional indices.

$a^{-m} = \dfrac{1}{a^m}$

$(c^2)^{-3} = c^{2 \times -3} = c^{-6} = \dfrac{1}{c^6}$

$a^{\frac{1}{n}} = \sqrt[n]{a}$

$(8p^3)^{\frac{1}{3}} = (8)^{\frac{1}{3}} \times (p^3)^{\frac{1}{3}}$
$\qquad\qquad = \sqrt[3]{8} \times p^{3 \times \frac{1}{3}}$
$\qquad\qquad = 2p$

One at a time

When you are MULTIPLYING expressions:

1. Multiply any number parts first.

2. Add the powers of each letter to work out the new power.

$$6p^2q \times 3p^3q^2 = 18p^5q^3$$

$6 \times 3 = 18$

$p^2 \times p^3 = p^{2+3} = p^5$

$q \times q^2 = q^{1+2} = q^3$

When you are DIVIDING expressions:

1. Divide any number parts first.

2. Subtract the powers of each letter to work out the new power.

$12 \div 3 = 4$

$b^3 \div b^2 = b^{3-2} = b$

$$\dfrac{12a^5b^3}{3a^2b^2} = 4a^3b$$

$a^5 \div a^2 = a^{5-2} = a^3$

Worked example

Simplify fully

(a) $m \times m \times m \times m$ **(1 mark)**

m^4

(b) $(x^3)^3$ **(1 mark)**

x^9

(c) $\dfrac{4y^2 \times 3y^7}{6y}$ **(2 marks)**

$\dfrac{4y^2 \times 3y^7}{6y} = \dfrac{12y^9}{6y} = 2y^8$

(a) $m = m^1$, so $m \times m \times m \times m$
$\qquad = m^{1+1+1+1}$

(b) Use $(a^m)^n = a^{mn}$

(c) Start by simplifying the top part of the fraction. Do the number part first then the powers. Use $a^m \times a^n = a^{m+n}$

Next divide the expressions. Divide the number part, then divide the indices using $\dfrac{a^m}{a^n} = a^{m-n}$

Now try this

1 Simplify $(h^2)^6$ **(1 mark)**

2 Simplify fully
  (a) $(2a^5b)^4$ **(2 marks)**
  (b) $5x^4y^2 \times 3x^3y^7$ **(2 marks)**
  (c) $18d^8g^{10} \div 6d^2g^5$ **(2 marks)**

 Aiming higher

3 Simplify $(25p^6)^{\frac{1}{2}}$ fully.   **(2 marks)**

Remember you need to apply the power outside the brackets to everything inside the brackets.

Expanding brackets

Expanding or multiplying out brackets is a key algebra skill.

You have to multiply the expression outside the bracket by everything inside the bracket.

$4n \times n^2 = 4n^3$

$$4n(n^2 + 2) = 4n^3 + 8n$$

$4n \times 2 = 8n$

'Expand and simplify' means 'multiply out and then collect like terms'.

Golden rule

When you expand, you need to be careful with negative signs in front of the bracket.

Negative signs belong to the term to their right.

$-2 \times x$ $-2 \times -y$

$$x - 2(x - y) = x - 2x + 2y$$
$$= -x + 2y$$

Multiply out the brackets first and then collect like terms if possible.

You can use the GRID METHOD to expand two brackets.

$(x + 7)(x - 5) = x^2 - 5x + 7x - 35$
$$= x^2 + 2x - 35$$

Remember to collect like terms if possible.

	x	−5
x	x^2	−5x
7	7x	−35

The negative sign belongs to the 5.

You need to write it in your grid.

OR

You can use the acronym FOIL to expand two brackets.

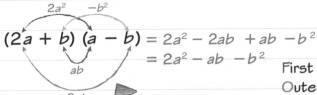

$2a^2$ $-b^2$

$(2a + b)(a - b) = 2a^2 - 2ab + ab - b^2$
$$= 2a^2 - ab - b^2$$

ab

$-2ab$

First terms
Outer terms
Inner terms
Last terms

Some people remember this as a 'smiley face'.

Worked example

Expand and simplify $(3p - 4)^2$ **(2 marks)**

$(3p - 4)^2 = (3p - 4)(3p - 4)$
$$= 9p^2 - 12p - 12p + 16$$
$$= 9p^2 - 24p + 16$$

	3p	−4
3p	$9p^2$	−12p
−4	−12p	16

EXAM ALERT!

The question is 'expand and simplify' so you have to multiply out **and** collect like terms.

Use the grid method or FOIL or another method to find all four terms of the expansion.

Be extra careful with your negative signs:

$-4 \times -4 = 16$ $p \times -4 = -4p$

Students have struggled with exam questions similar to this – **be prepared!**

Now try this

1 Expand $5(a - 6)$ **(2 marks)**

2 Expand and simplify
  (a) $3(2b - 1) - 4(b + 2)$ **(2 marks)**
  (b) $8y(3y^3 + 4)$ **(2 marks)**
  (c) $2x(x^2 + 6) + 3x(x - 5)$ **(3 marks)**
  (d) $(m + 9)(m - 3)$ **(2 marks)**

Aiming higher

3 Expand and simplify
  (a) $(3g - 4e)(2g - 5e)$ **(2 marks)**
  (b) $(4x + 7)^2$ **(2 marks)**

$(4x + 7)^2 = (4x + 7)(4x + 7)$

Factorising

Factorising is the opposite of expanding brackets:

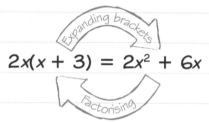

$$2x(x + 3) = 2x^2 + 6x$$

You need to look for the LARGEST FACTOR you can take out of every term in the expression.

$$10a^2 + 5ab = 5(2a^2 + ab)$$

This expression has only been PARTLY FACTORISED.

$$10a^2 + 5ab = 5a(2a + b)$$

This expression has been COMPLETELY FACTORISED.

Factorising $x^2 + bx + c$

You need to write the expression with TWO BRACKETS.

You need to find two numbers which add up to 7... $5 + 2 = 7$

$$x^2 + 7x + 10 = (x + 5)(x + 2)$$

... and multiply to make 10 $5 \times 2 = 10$

When factorising $x^2 + bx + c$, use this table to help you find the two numbers:

b	c	Factors
Positive	Positive	Both numbers positive
Positive	Negative	Bigger number positive and smaller number negative
Negative	Negative	Bigger number negative and smaller number positive
Negative	Positive	Both numbers negative

Factorising $ax^2 + bx + c$

$$2x^2 - 7x - 15 = (2x \quad)(x \quad)$$

One of the brackets must contain a $2x$ term. Try pairs of numbers which have a product of -15. Check each pair by multiplying out the brackets.

$(2x + 5)(x - 3) = 2x^2 - x - 15$ ✗
$(2x - 3)(x + 5) = 2x^2 + 7x - 15$ ✗
$(2x + 3)(x - 5) = 2x^2 - 7x - 15$ ✓

Difference of two squares

You can factorise expressions that are written as

$$(\text{something})^2 - (\text{something else})^2$$

Use this rule:
$$a^2 - b^2 = (a + b)(a - b)$$
$$x^2 - 36 = x^2 - (6)^2$$
$$= (x + 6)(x - 6)$$

36 is a square number.

$36 = 6^2$ so $a = x$ and $b = 6$

Worked example

Factorise fully
(a) $p^2 - 3p$
    (2 marks)
(b) $15x^2 + 5xy$
    (2 marks)

$p(p - 3)$

$5x(3x + y)$

You need to look for the **largest** factor you can take out of every term.
Partly factorised: $x(15x + 5y)$ ✗
Partly factorised: $5(3x^2 + xy)$ ✗
Fully factorised: $5x(3x + y)$ ✓

Now try this

1 Factorise
   (a) $4a - 6$ **(1 mark)**
   (b) $y^2 + 5y$ **(1 mark)**

2 Factorise fully
   (a) $12g + 3g^2$ **(2 marks)**
   (b) $p^2 - 15p + 14$ **(2 marks)**
   (c) $6x^2 - 8xy$ **(2 marks)**

3 Factorise
   (a) $4ma - 24m^2a$ **(2 marks)**
   (b) $p^2 - 64$ **(1 mark)**

Aiming higher

4 Factorise fully
   (a) $3y^2 + 7y - 20$ **(2 marks)**
   (b) $x^2 - 81y^2$ **(2 marks)**
   (c) $50g^2 - 2e^2$ **(3 marks)**

Algebraic fractions

Simplifying an algebraic fraction is just like simplifying a normal fraction.

You can divide the top and bottom by a number, a term, or a whole expression.

> **Golden rule**
>
> If the top or the bottom of the fraction has MORE THAN one term, you will need to factorise before simplifying.
>
> $$\frac{p^2 + 3p}{4p} = \frac{p(p + 3)}{4p} = \frac{p + 3}{4}$$
>
> Two terms on top so factorise the top, then divide the top and bottom by p.

Operations on algebraic fractions

1 To ADD or SUBTRACT algebraic fractions with different denominators:

1. Find a common denominator.
2. Add or subtract the numerators.
3. Simplify if possible.

$$\frac{1}{x + 4} + \frac{2}{x - 4} = \frac{x - 4}{(x + 4)(x - 4)} + \frac{2(x + 4)}{(x + 4)(x - 4)}$$

$$= \frac{x - 4 + 2x + 8}{(x + 4)(x - 4)} = \frac{3x + 4}{(x + 4)(x - 4)}$$

The smallest common denominator isn't always the product of the two denominators.

You can use a common denominator of $4x$

to simplify this expression:

$$\frac{x + 1}{2x} + \frac{3 - 2x}{4x}$$

2 To MULTIPLY fractions:

1. Multiply the numerators AND multiply the denominators.
2. Simplify if possible.

$$\frac{x}{2} \times \frac{4}{x - 1} = \frac{\overset{2}{\cancel{4}}x}{\underset{1}{\cancel{2}}(x - 1)} = \frac{2x}{x - 1}$$

Don't expand brackets if you don't have to. It's much easier to simplify your fraction with the brackets in place.

3 To DIVIDE fractions:

1. Change the second fraction to its reciprocal.
2. Change ÷ to ×
3. Multiply the fractions and simplify.

$$\frac{x^2}{3} \div \frac{x}{6} = \frac{x^2}{3} \times \frac{6}{x} = \frac{\overset{2}{\cancel{6}}x^2}{\underset{1}{\cancel{3}}x} = 2x$$

To find the reciprocal of a fraction you turn it upside down.

Simplify $\dfrac{3x^2 - 8x - 3}{x^2 - 9}$ **(3 marks)**

Aiming higher

$$\frac{3x^2 - 8x - 3}{x^2 - 9} = \frac{(3x + 1)(x - 3)}{(x + 3)(x - 3)}$$

$$= \frac{3x + 1}{x + 3}$$

You need to factorise the top and the bottom of the fraction before you can simplify. Remember that $a^2 - b^2 = (a + b)(a - b)$

Students have struggled with exam questions similar to this – **be prepared!**

Aiming higher

1 Simplify fully

(a) $\dfrac{a + 1}{3a} + \dfrac{7}{6a}$ **(3 marks)**

(b) $\dfrac{3y}{(y - 3)(y + 6)} - \dfrac{2}{y + 6}$ **(4 marks)**

Aiming higher

2 Simplify fully

(a) $\dfrac{x^2 + 4x - 12}{x^2 - 25} \div \dfrac{x + 6}{x^2 - 5x}$ **(4 marks)**

(b) $\dfrac{3m^2 - 108}{9m^3 + 54m^2}$ **(3 marks)**

Surds 2

You might need to expand brackets involving surds. You can use the grid method, or FOIL to expand the brackets (have a look at p. 21). Here are two GOLDEN RULES to remember when working with surds.

 1 You can use the rule $\sqrt{ab} = \sqrt{a} \times \sqrt{b}$ in BOTH DIRECTIONS:

$\sqrt{20} \times \sqrt{5} = \sqrt{100} = 10$

$\sqrt{2a} \times \sqrt{18a} = \sqrt{36a^2} = \sqrt{36} \times \sqrt{a^2} = 6a$

 2 Whole number parts and surd parts stay SEPARATE:

If $24 + 6\sqrt{7} = a + b\sqrt{7}$ then you can COMPARE the two expressions to get $a = 24$ and $b = 6$

Worked example

Show that $(3 + \sqrt{8})(4 + \sqrt{8}) = 20 + 14\sqrt{2}$

Show each stage of your working clearly. **(2 marks)**

$(3 + \sqrt{8})(4 + \sqrt{8}) = 12 + 3\sqrt{8} + 4\sqrt{8} + (\sqrt{8})^2$
$= 20 + 7\sqrt{8}$
$= 20 + 7 \times 2\sqrt{2}$
$= 20 + 14\sqrt{2}$

When the question says "Show that…" you should start from the **left-hand side**, then simplify and rearrange until your expression matches the **right-hand side**.

Make sure you **simplify** any surds in your expression:

$\sqrt{8} = \sqrt{4 \times 2}$
$= \sqrt{4} \times \sqrt{2}$
$= 2\sqrt{2}$

There's more about this on page 14.

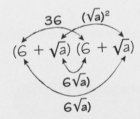

Simplify the expression, remembering that $(\sqrt{a})^2 = a$, then compare your answer with the right-hand side given in the question. $12\sqrt{a} = 12\sqrt{2}$ so $a = 2$, and $36 + a = b$ so $b = 38$

Worked example

Given that a and b are positive integers such that $(6 + \sqrt{a})^2 = b + 12\sqrt{2}$

find the value of a and the value of b. **(3 marks)**

$(6 + \sqrt{a}^2) = (6 + \sqrt{a})(6 + \sqrt{a})$
$= 36 + 6\sqrt{a} + 6\sqrt{a} + (\sqrt{a})^2$
$= 36 + a + 12\sqrt{a}$
$= b + 12\sqrt{2}$

$a = 2$ and $b = 38$

Now try this

1 Show that $(3 - \sqrt{12})^2 = 21 - 12\sqrt{3}$

Show each stage of your working clearly. **(3 marks)**

Aiming higher

2 $(5 + \sqrt{x})(3 + \sqrt{x}) = 18 + k\sqrt{x}$

where x is a prime number and k is a positive integer.

Find the value of x and the value of k. **(3 marks)**

Straight-line graphs

Here are three things you need to know about straight-line graphs.

 If an equation is in the form $y = mx + c$, its graph will be a straight line.

$$y = -\tfrac{1}{2}x + 5$$

This number tells you the gradient of the graph.

The y-intercept of the graph is at (0, 5).

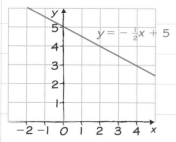

The gradient of the graph is $-\tfrac{1}{2}$
This means that for every unit you go across, you go half a unit down.

 Use a table of values to draw a graph.

$y = 2x + 1$

x	−1	0	1	2
y	−1	1	3	5

$y = 2 \times 2 + 1 = 5$

Choose simple values of x and substitute them into the equation to find the values of y.

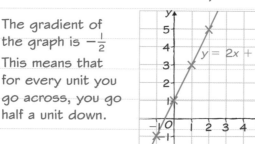

Plot the points on your graph and join them with a straight line.

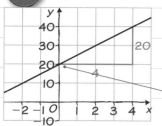 You need to be able to find the equation of a line.

Draw a triangle to find the gradient.

Gradient $= \dfrac{20}{4} = 5$

The y-intercept is at (0, 20)

Put your values for m and c into the equation of a straight line, $y = mx + c$

The equation is $y = 5x + 20$

Straight-line checklist

Plot at least three points when drawing straight-line graphs.

Lines of the form $y = mx$ pass through (0, 0)   ✓

Lines of the form $y = mx + c$ pass through the y-axis at (0, c)   ✓

m is positive, line slopes up.   ✓

m is negative, line slopes down.   ✓

Worked example

Aiming higher

A line passes through the points with coordinates (1, 5) and (2, 7).

Find the equation of the line.

(3 marks)

Gradient, $m = \dfrac{2}{1} = 2$

Equation of line: $y = mx + c \rightarrow y = 2x + c$

For point (1, 5), $x = 1$, $y = 5$

Substitute these values into the equation:

$5 = 2 + c \rightarrow c = 3$

The equation is $y = 2x + 3$

Follow these steps:
1. Draw a **sketch** of the straight line.
2. Draw a **triangle** to find the gradient. This is your value for m. Put it into the equation for the line.
3. Use the x- and y-values of one of the points on the line to write an equation.
4. **Solve** your equation to find c.

Now try this

The points (0, −3) and (6, 1) lie on the straight line **L**.
(a) Work out the gradient of **L**.   **(2 marks)**
(b) Write down an equation of **L**.   **(1 mark)**

The gradient doesn't have to be a whole number. The line passes through (0, −3) so you know the y-intercept.

Parallel lines

PARALLEL lines have the same gradient.
These three lines all have a gradient of 1.

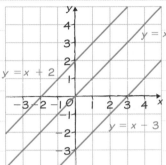

Parallel lines NEVER MEET.

Midpoints

A LINE SEGMENT is a short section of a straight line. You can find the MIDPOINT of a line segment if you know the coordinates of the ends.

Coordinates of midpoint = (average of x-coordinates, average of y-coordinates)

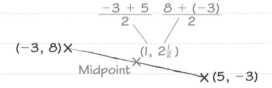

On the grid, M is the midpoint of the line segment PQ. The gradient of PQ is $\frac{1}{2}$

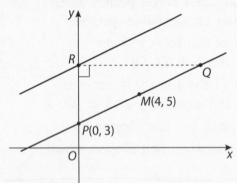

Work out the equation of the line through R that is parallel to PQ.   **(3 marks)**

$5 - 3 = 2$ $5 + 2 = 7$

The y-coordinate of Q and R is 7

The line has equation $y = \frac{1}{2}x + 7$

You need to work out the y-coordinate of Q. You know that M is the midpoint so the vertical distance from P to M is the same as the distance from M to Q.

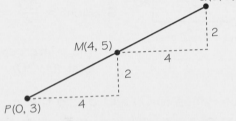

R is level with Q so it has the same y-coordinate. Because the line through R is parallel to PQ it has the same gradient, $\frac{1}{2}$

You know the gradient and y-intercept of the line so you can write down its equation using $y = mx + c$

---

1 The point A has coordinates $(2, -1)$ and the point B has coordinates $(6, 3)$
M is the midpoint of the line segment AB.

(a) Find the coordinates of M.   **(2 marks)**

(b) Find the equation of a line that passes through M and has gradient $-\frac{1}{2}$ **(2 marks)**

2 The points $(0, 1)$ and $(8, 3)$ lie on the straight line **L**.

(a) Work out the gradient of **L**.   **(2 marks)**

(b) Write down an equation of **L**.   **(1 mark)**

(c) Find an equation of the line which is parallel to **L** and which passes through the point $(-4, -1)$ **(2 marks)**

Formulae

A FORMULA is a mathematical rule.

You can write formulae using algebra.

This label shows a formula for working out the cooking time of a chicken.

You can write this formula using algebra as

FREE-RANGE CHICKEN		
WEIGHT (KG)	**PRICE PER KG**	**COOKING INSTRUCTIONS**
1.8	£3.95	Cook at 170°C for 25 minutes per kg plus half an hour

$T = 25w + 30$, where T is the cooking time in minutes and w is the weight in kg.

In the description of each variable, you must give the units.

If T was the cooking time in hours then this formula would give you a very crispy chicken!

Worked example

This formula is used in physics to calculate distance:

$D = ut - 5t^2$

$u = 14$ and $t = -3$

Work out the value of D. **(2 marks)**

$D = (14)(-3) - 5(-3)^2$

$\quad = (14)(-3) - 5(9)$

$\quad = -42 - 45$

$\quad = -87$

Substitute the values for u and t into the formula.

If you use brackets then you're less likely to make a mistake. This is really important when there are negative numbers involved.

Remember **BIDMAS** for the correct order of operations. You need to do:

Indices → **M**ultiplication → **S**ubtraction

Don't try to do more than one operation on each line of working.

Worked example

This rule can be used to convert temperatures in degrees Celsius (°C) into degrees Fahrenheit (°F).

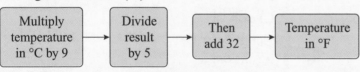

| Multiply temperature in °C by 9 | → | Divide result by 5 | → | Then add 32 | → | Temperature in °F |

Write this rule as an algebraic formula. **(2 marks)**

$F = \dfrac{9C}{5} + 32$

Make sure that your formula starts with "$F =$". If you just wrote $\dfrac{9C}{5} + 32$ you would have written an **expression**, not a **formula**.

Check it!

Convert a temperature from °C using the rule and your formula and check you get the same answer.

Now try this

The perimeter of this shape can be calculated using the formula

$$P = \frac{4(a^2 + ab + b^2)}{a + b}$$

Find the value of P when $a = 4.3$ cm and $b = 2.9$ cm.
Give your answer correct to 3 significant figures.

(2 marks)

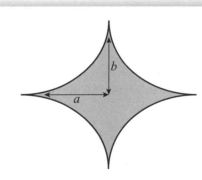

Linear equations 1

To solve a linear equation you need to get the letter on its own on one side.
It is really important to write your working NEATLY when you are solving equations.

$$5x + 3 = 18 \quad (-3)$$
$$5x = 15 \quad (\div 3)$$
$$x = 3$$

Every line of working should have an equals sign in it.

Write down the operation you are carrying out. Remember to do the same thing to both sides of the equation.

Start a new line for each step.
Do one operation at a time.

Line up the equals signs.

Letter on both sides?

To solve an equation you have to get the letter on its own on one side of the equation.

Start by collecting like terms so that all the letters are together.

$$2 - 2x = 26 + 4x \quad (+ 2x)$$
$$2 = 26 + 6x \quad (- 26)$$
$$-24 = 6x \quad (\div 6)$$
$$-4 = x$$

You can write your answer as

$-4 = x$ or as $x = -4$

Equations with brackets

Always start by multiplying out the brackets then collecting like terms.

For a reminder about multiplying out brackets have a look at page 21.

$$19 = 8 - 2(5 - 3y)$$
$$19 = 8 - 10 + 6y$$
$$19 = -2 + 6y \quad (+ 2)$$
$$21 = 6y \quad (\div 6)$$
$$\frac{21}{6} = y$$
$$y = \frac{7}{2} \text{ or } 3\frac{1}{2} \text{ or } 3.5$$

Your answer can be written as a fraction or decimal.

Worked example

Solve $7r + 2 = 5(r - 4)$
Show clear algebraic working.   (3 marks)

$$7r + 2 = 5r - 20 \quad (- 5r)$$
$$2r + 2 = -20 \quad (- 2)$$
$$2r = -22 \quad (\div 2)$$
$$r = -11$$

Multiply out the brackets then collect all the terms in r on one side.

Check it!

Substitute $r = -11$ into each side of the equation.

Left-hand side: $7(-11) + 2 = -75$
Right-hand side: $5(-11 - 4) = -75$ ✓

Now try this

1 Solve

(a) $5w - 17 = 2w + 4$ (3 marks)

(b) $2(x + 11) = 20$ (3 marks)

Show clear algebraic working.

Expand the brackets first.

2 Solve

(a) $6y - 9 = 2(y - 8)$ (3 marks)

(b) $4m - 2(m - 3) = 7m - 14$ (3 marks)

Show clear algebraic working.

Expand the brackets then collect all the m terms on one side of the equation.

Linear equations 2

Equations with fractions

When you have an equation with fractions, you need to get rid of any fractions before solving. You can do this by multiplying every term by the lowest common multiple (LCM) of the denominators.

$$\frac{x}{3} + \frac{x-1}{5} = 11 \qquad (\times 15)$$

The LCM of 3 and 5 is 15.

$$\frac{{}^5\cancel{15}x}{\cancel{3}_1} + \frac{{}^3\cancel{15}(x-1)}{\cancel{5}_1} = 165$$

Cancel the fractions. There is more about simplifying algebraic fractions on page 38.

$$5x + 3x - 3 = 165$$
$$8x - 3 = 165 \qquad (+3)$$
$$8x = 168 \qquad (\div 8)$$
$$x = 21$$

Multiplying by an expression

You might have to multiply by an expression to get rid of the fractions.

$$\frac{20}{n-3} = -5 \qquad (\times(n-3))$$
$$20 = -5(n-3)$$

Worked example

Solve $\dfrac{29-x}{4} = x + 5$ **(3 marks)**

Show clear algebraic working.

$$\frac{4(29-x)}{4} = 4(x+5)$$
$$29 - x = 4(x+5)$$
$$29 - x = 4x + 20 \qquad (+x)$$
$$29 = 5x + 20 \qquad (-20)$$
$$9 = 5x \qquad (\div 5)$$
$$\frac{9}{5} = x$$

EXAM ALERT!

You need to get rid of any fractions **before** you start solving the equation. Multiply both sides of the equation by 4. Use brackets to show that you are multiplying everything by 4.

$$4(x+5) \checkmark \qquad 4x + 5 ✗$$

Multiply out the brackets and solve normally. Your answer can be a whole number or a fraction.

Check it!
If you have time, check each line of your working carefully.

Students have struggled with exam questions similar to this – **be prepared!**

Writing your own equations

You can find unknown values by writing and solving equations.

$4(x-1)$ cm $(3x+3)$ cm

$\frac{5}{n}$ m   Perimeter = 20 m   2 m

$$4(x-1) = 3x + 3 \qquad \frac{5}{n} + \frac{5}{n} + 2 + 2 = 20$$

Now try this

1 Solve

(a) $\dfrac{25-3w}{4} = 10$ **(3 marks)**

(b) $5x - 10 = \dfrac{18-x}{3}$ **(3 marks)**

Show clear algebraic working.

2 Solve

(a) $\dfrac{2y}{3} + \dfrac{y-4}{2} = 5$ **(3 marks)**

(b) $\dfrac{3m-1}{4} - \dfrac{2m+4}{3} = 1.5$ **(3 marks)**

Show clear algebraic working.

Rearranging formulae

Most formulae have one letter on its own on one side of the formula. This letter is called the SUBJECT of the formula.

$$e = mc^2$$ e is the subject of the formula.

CHANGING THE SUBJECT of a formula is like solving an equation. You have to do the same thing to both sides of the formula until you have the new letter on its own on one side.

$$e = mc^2 \qquad (\div m)$$

$$\frac{e}{m} = c^2 \qquad (\sqrt{\ })$$

$$\sqrt{\frac{e}{m}} = c$$

The inverse operation to x^2 is $\sqrt{\square}$.
You need to square root EVERYTHING on both sides of the formula.

c is now the subject of the formula.

Harder formulae

If the letter you need APPEARS TWICE in the formula you need to FACTORISE.

| GROUP all the terms with that letter on one side of the formula and all the other terms on the other side. | → | FACTORISE so the letter only appears once. | → | DIVIDE by everything in the bracket to get the letter on its own. |

For a reminder about factorising have a look at page 22.

 Worked example

$$N = \frac{3h + 20}{100}$$

Rearrange the formula to make h the subject.

(3 marks)

$$N = \frac{3h + 20}{100} \qquad (\times 100)$$

$$100N = 3h + 20 \qquad (- 20)$$

$$100N - 20 = 3h \qquad (\div 3)$$

$$\frac{100N - 20}{3} = h$$

$$h = \frac{100N - 20}{3}$$

It's a good idea to write your final answer as $h = \dots$

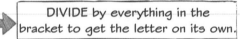 **Worked example**

Make Q the subject of the formula $P = \dfrac{Q}{Q - 100}$

 Aiming higher

(4 marks)

$$P = \frac{Q}{Q - 100} \qquad [\times (Q - 100)]$$

$$P(Q - 100) = Q \qquad \text{(multiply out brackets)}$$

$$PQ - 100P = Q \qquad (+ 100P)$$

$$PQ = Q + 100P \qquad (- Q)$$

$$PQ - Q = 100P \qquad \text{(factorise)}$$

$$Q(P - 1) = 100P \qquad [\div (P - 1)]$$

$$Q = \frac{100P}{P - 1}$$

Your final answer should look like $Q = \dots$
You need to factorise to get Q on its own.

Now try this

1 Rearrange this formula to make t the subject.

$$4p = 3t - 1 \qquad \textbf{(2 marks)}$$

2 Make w the subject of $m = \sqrt{5w + 7}$

(3 marks)

 Aiming higher

3 Make y the subject of $x = \dfrac{5 - 9y}{y + 2}$

(4 marks)

Square both sides first.

Inequalities

An inequality tells you when one value is bigger or smaller than another value.
You can represent INEQUALITIES on a number line.

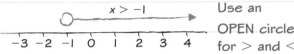

$x > -1$

Use an OPEN circle for $>$ and $<$

The open circle shows that -1 is NOT included.

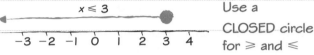

$x \leq 3$

Use a CLOSED circle for $\geq$ and $\leq$

The closed circle shows that 3 IS included.

Solving inequalities

You can solve an inequality in exactly the same way as you solve an equation.

$x - 3 \leq 12 \quad (+ 3)$
$\quad x \leq 15$

The solution has the letter on its own on one side of the inequality and a number on the other side.

Golden rule

If you MULTIPLY or DIVIDE both sides of an inequality by a NEGATIVE number you have to REVERSE the INEQUALITY sign.

$6 - 5x > 10 \quad (- 6)$
$\quad -5x > 4 \quad (\div -5)$
$\qquad x < \dfrac{-4}{5}$

You have divided by a negative number so you have to reverse the inequality sign.

Worked example

Solve $8x - 7 > 3x + 3$ **(2 marks)**

$\qquad\qquad\qquad (+ 7)$
$8x > 3x + 10 \quad (- 3x)$
$5x > 10 \qquad (\div 5)$
$\quad x > 2$

EXAM ALERT!

This is an **inequality** and not an equation. You must not use an '$=$' sign in your answer. Remember that the solution has the letter on its own on one side and a number on the other side.

Students have struggled with exam questions similar to this – **be prepared!**

Integer solutions

You might need to write down all the integer solutions that SATISFY an inequality.
INTEGERS are positive or negative whole numbers, including O.

$-3 \leq x < 2$

This shows that x is between -3 and 2. It can equal -3 but cannot equal 2.

The integer solutions that satisfy this inequality are $-3, -2, -1, 0$ and 1.

Now try this

1 n is an integer. Write down all the values of n which satisfy $-9 < 3n \leq 6$ **(2 marks)**

2 n is an integer. Write down all the values of n which satisfy $0 \leq n + 4 < 5$ **(2 marks)**

3 Solve the inequality $3n + 8 > 2$ **(2 marks)**

4 Solve the inequality $2(n - 5) \geq n + 12$ **(2 marks)**

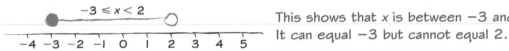

Start by multiplying out the brackets. Then subtract n from both sides to get the letter on its own.

Inequalities on graphs

You can show the points that satisfy inequalities involving x and y on a graph.

For example, follow these steps to shade the region R that satisfies the inequalities:

$$x \geqslant 2 \qquad y \geqslant x \qquad x + y \geqslant 6$$

Always work on one inequality at a time.

 1

$x \geqslant 2$

Draw the graph of $x = 2$

Use a small arrow to show which side of the line you want.

2

$y \geqslant x$

Draw the graph of $y = x$

Show which side of the line you want.

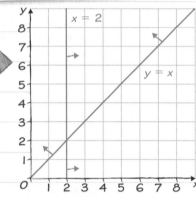

3

$x + y \geqslant 6$

Draw the graph of $x + y = 6$. Use a table of values.

x	0	3	6
y	6	3	0

Show which side of the line you want.

$x + y$ increases as you move away from the origin.

Shade in the region and label it **R**.

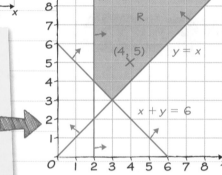

Horizontal and vertical lines

Horizontal lines have equation $y = \square$

Vertical lines have equation $x = \square$

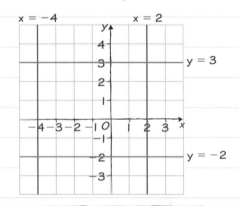

Always check your answer

Pick a point inside your shaded region.

Check that the x- and y-values for that point satisfy **all** the inequalities.

At $(4, 5)$ $x = 4$ and $y = 5$

$x \geqslant 2$ ✓ $\qquad y \geqslant x$ ✓ $\qquad x + y \geqslant 6$ ✓

Students have struggled with exam questions similar to this – **be prepared!**

Now try this

You can shade either inside or outside the region, but make sure you label your region **R**.

Show, by shading on a grid, the region defined by all three of these inequalities. Label your region **R**.

$y \geqslant 1$

$y \leqslant 2x + 1$

$2x + 3y \leqslant 12$ (4 marks)

Quadratic graphs

An equation in x where the highest power is a term in x^2 is called a QUADRATIC equation. Quadratic equations have CURVED graphs. You can draw the graph of a quadratic equation by completing a table of values.

Worked example

(a) Complete the table of values for $y = 4x - x^2$ **(2 marks)**

x	−1	0	1	2	3	4	5
y	−5	0	3	4	3	0	−5

(b) On the grid, draw the graph of $y = 4x - x^2$ **(2 marks)**

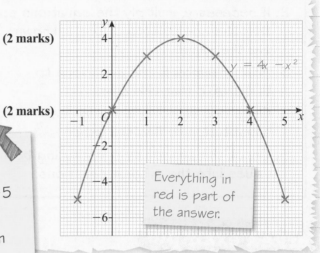

Substitute each value of x into the equation to get a corresponding value of y.

When $x = -1$: $4 \times -1 - (-1)^2 = -4 - 1 = -5$

When $x = 4$: $4 \times 4 - (4)^2 = 16 - 16 = 0$

Plot your points carefully on the graph and join them with a **smooth** curve.

Check it!
All the points on your graph should lie on the curve. If one of the points doesn't fit then double-check your calculation.

Everything in red is part of the answer.

Drawing quadratic curves
Use a sharp pencil. ✓
Plot the points carefully. ✓
Draw a smooth curve that passes through every point. ✓
Label your graph. ✓
Shape of graph will be either or ⌒

Drawing a smooth curve
It's easier to draw a smooth curve if you turn your graph paper so your hand is INSIDE the curve.

Now try this

(a) Complete the table of values for $y = x^2 - 2x - 4$

x	−2	−1	0	1	2	3	4
y		−1	−4			−1	4

(2 marks)

(b) On the grid, draw the graph of $y = x^2 - 2x - 4$ **(2 marks)**

(c) On the grid, draw the graph of $y = 1$ **(1 mark)**

(d) Write down estimates for the coordinates of the points of intersection of the two graphs. Give your answers correct to 1 decimal place.

(2 marks)

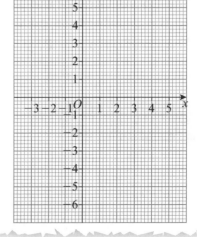

Simultaneous equations 1

Simultaneous equations have two unknowns. You need to find the values for the two unknowns which make BOTH equations true.

Algebraic solution

1. Number each equation.

2. If necessary, multiply the equations so that the coefficients of one unknown are the same.

3. Add or subtract the equations to ELIMINATE that unknown.

4. Once one unknown is found use substitution to find the other.

5. Check the answer by substituting both values into the original equations.

$$3x + y = 20 \quad \text{(I)}$$
$$x + 4y = 14 \quad \text{(2)}$$

$$12x + 4y = 80 \quad \text{(I)} \times 4$$
$$- (x + 4y = 14) \quad - \text{(2)}$$
$$\overline{11x = 66}$$
$$x = 6$$

Substitute $x = 6$ into (I):
$$3(6) + y = 20$$
$$18 + y = 20$$
$$y = 2$$

Solution is $x = 6$, $y = 2$
Check: $x + 4y = 6 + 4(2) = 14$ ✓

Worked example

Solve the simultaneous equations
$$6x + 2y = -3 \quad \text{(I)}$$
$$4x - 3y = 11 \quad \text{(2)} \qquad \textbf{(4 marks)}$$

$$18x + 6y = -9 \quad \text{(I)} \times 3$$
$$+ \ 8x - 6y = 22 \quad \text{(2)} \times 2$$
$$\overline{26x = 13}$$
$$x = \tfrac{1}{2}$$

Substitute $x = \tfrac{1}{2}$ into (I):
$$6\left(\tfrac{1}{2}\right) + 2y = -3$$
$$3 + 2y = -3$$
$$2y = -6$$
$$y = -3$$

EXAM ALERT!

When deciding which unknown to eliminate, if possible choose the unknown where the signs are different. You can then eliminate the unknown by adding the equations.

Multiply both equations by a whole number to make the coefficients the same.

Check it!
Always use the equation you didn't substitute into to check.
$$4x - 3y = 4\left(\tfrac{1}{2}\right) - 3(-3) = 2 + 9 = 11 ✓$$

Students have struggled with exam questions similar to this – **be prepared!**

Graphical solution

You can solve these simultaneous equations by drawing a graph.
$$x - y = 1 \qquad x + 2y = 4$$
The coordinates of the point of intersection give the solution to the simultaneous equations.

The solution is $x = 2$, $y = 1$

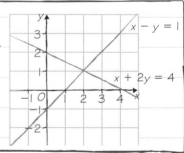

Now try this

1 Solve the simultaneous equations
$$3x - 2y = 12$$
$$x + 4y = 11$$
   Show clear algebraic working. **(3 marks)**

2 Solve the simultaneous equations
$$2x - 3y = 11$$
$$3x + 4y = 8$$
   Show clear algebraic working. **(4 marks)**

Quadratic equations

Quadratic equations can be written in the form $ax^2 + bx + c = 0$ where a, b and c are numbers.

You need to be able to SOLVE a quadratic equation without using your calculator.

1. REARRANGE it into the form $ax^2 + bx + c = 0$
2. FACTORISE the left-hand side.
3. Set each factor EQUAL TO ZERO and solve to find two values of x.

For a reminder about factorising quadratic expressions have a look at page 22.

Two to watch

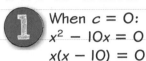

1. When $c = 0$:
$$x^2 - 10x = 0$$
$$x(x - 10) = 0$$
Solutions are $x = 0$ and $x = 10$

2. When $b = 0$ (difference of two squares):
$$9x^2 - 4 = 0$$
$$(3x + 2)(3x - 2) = 0$$
Solutions are $x = \frac{2}{3}$ and $x = -\frac{2}{3}$

Worked example

Solve $x^2 + 8x - 9 = 0$
Show clear algebraic working.   **(3 marks)**

$$(x + 9)(x - 1) = 0$$

$x + 9 = 0 \qquad\qquad x - 1 = 0$

$x = -9 \qquad\qquad\quad x = 1$

Follow the three steps given above.

1. The equation is already in the right form.

2. To factorise look for two numbers which add up to 8 and multiply to make -9. The numbers are 9 and -1.

3. Set each factor equal to 0 and solve.

Check it!
$(1)^2 + 8(1) - 9 = 1 + 8 - 9 = 0$ ✓
$(-9)^2 + 8(-9) - 9 = 81 - 72 - 9 = 0$ ✓

Worked example   Aiming higher

Solve $2(x + 1)^2 = 3x + 5$
Show clear algebraic working.   **(4 marks)**

$$2(x^2 + 2x + 1) = 3x + 5$$
$$2x^2 + 4x + 2 = 3x + 5$$
$$2x^2 + x - 3 = 0$$
$$(2x + 3)(x - 1) = 0$$

$2x + 3 = 0 \qquad\qquad x - 1 = 0$

$x = -\frac{3}{2} \qquad\qquad\quad x = 1$

EXAM ALERT!

When you are solving a quadratic equation you must rearrange it into the form $ax^2 + bx + c = 0$ **before** you factorise.

Be really careful if the coefficient of x^2 is bigger than 1. The two factors will look like this:
$$2x^2 + x - 3 = 0$$
$$(2x \pm \dots)(x \pm \dots) = 0$$

The number part of the expression is -3, so the numbers in the factors must be either -1 and 3 or 1 and -3.

Students have struggled with exam questions similar to this – **be prepared!**

Now try this

Solve, showing clear algebraic working

(a) $m^2 - 8m + 12 = 0$ **(3 marks)**

(b) $w^2 - 36 = 5w$ **(3 marks)**

Aiming higher

(c) $5y^2 + 37y - 24 = 0$ **(3 marks)**

(d) $8x^2 - 4 = (x - 1)^2$ **(4 marks)**

The quadratic formula

This is how the quadratic formula will appear on the formula sheet in your exam.

The Quadratic Equation

The solutions of $ax^2 + bx + c = 0$

where $a \neq 0$, are given by

$$x = \frac{-b \pm \sqrt{(b^2 - 4ac)}}{2a}$$

If you're going for a top grade, you may need to use this in a problem-solving question.

Safe substituting

Equation is in the form
$ax^2 + bx + c = 0$ ✓

Write down your values of a, b and c before you substitute.   ✓

Use brackets when you are substituting negative numbers.

Show what you have substituted in the formula.

Simplify what is under the square root and write this down.

The $\pm$ symbol means you need to do two calculations.   ✓

Worked example

Aiming higher

Solve $5x^2 + x + 11 = 14$

Give your solutions correct to 3 significant figures.

Show your working clearly.   **(3 marks)**

$5x^2 + x - 3 = 0$

$a = 5, b = 1, c = -3$

$$x = -1 \pm \frac{\sqrt{1^2 - 4 \times 5 \times (-3)}}{2 \times 5}$$

$$= \frac{-1 + \sqrt{61}}{10} \text{ or } \frac{-1 - \sqrt{61}}{10}$$

$$= 0.681\,024... \text{ or } -0.881\,024...$$

$$= 0.681 \text{ or } -0.881 \text{ (to 3 s.f.)}$$

You are asked to find 'solution**s**'. This tells you that you are solving a quadratic equation.

You must give your answer 'correct to 3 significant figures'. This tells you that you need to use the quadratic formula. Turn to the formula sheet.

Write down at least five figures after the decimal point on the calculator display before giving your final answer. You might need to use the [S⇔D] button on your calculator to get your answer as a decimal.

How many solutions?

A quadratic equation can have two solutions, one solution or no solutions.
You can use $b^2 - 4ac$ (the part under the square root) to work out how many solutions a quadratic equation has.

If $b^2 - 4ac$ is negative, there are no solutions.   You can't calculate the square root of a negative number.

If $b^2 - 4ac = 0$ there is only one solution. ± 0 appears in the formula, so you get the same answer whether you use + or −

If $b^2 - 4ac > 0$ there are two different solutions.

Now try this

1 Solve $7x^2 + 3x - 6 = 0$

Give your solutions correct to 3 significant figures.   **(3 marks)**

2 Solve $m^2 + 50m = 6000$

Give your solutions correct to 3 significant figures.   **(3 marks)**

Quadratics and fractions

You need to remove fractions before you can solve an equation.

For a reminder about solving linear equations with fractions have a look at page 29.

To remove fractions from an equation multiply everything by the lowest common multiple of the denominators.

$$\frac{x}{2x-3} + \frac{4}{x+1} = 1$$

→ $(2x - 3)$ and $(x + 1)$ don't have any common factors. Multiply everything by $(2x - 3)(x + 1)$

$$\frac{x(2x-3)(x+1)}{2x-3} + \frac{4(2x-3)(x+1)}{x+1} = (2x-3)(x+1)$$

→ Don't expand brackets until you have simplified the fractions.

$$x(x+1) + 4(2x-3) = (2x-3)(x+1)$$

$$x^2 + x + 8x - 12 = 2x^2 - 3x + 2x - 3$$

$$0 = x^2 - 10x + 9$$

$$= (x-9)(x-1)$$

→ Multiply out brackets and collect like terms.

The solutions are $x = 9$ and $x = 1$

Worked example

Solve $\dfrac{2+3x}{5x+9} = \dfrac{2}{x-1}$ **(5 marks)**

$$\left(\frac{2+3x}{5x+9}\right)(x-1)(5x+9) = \left(\frac{2}{x-1}\right)(x-1)(5x+9)$$

Multiply everything by $(x - 1)(5x + 9)$ to remove the fractions.

$$\frac{(2+3x)(x-1)(5x+9)}{5x+9} = \frac{2(x-1)(5x+9)}{x-1}$$

If you are confident working with algebraic fractions you can jump straight to this step.

$$(2+3x)(x-1) = 2(5x+9)$$

$$3x^2 - 3x + 2x - 2 = 10x + 18$$

$$3x^2 - 11x - 20 = 0$$

$$(3x+4)(x-5) = 0$$

$$3x + 4 = 0 \qquad x - 5 = 0$$

$$x = -\frac{4}{3} \qquad x = 5$$

Set the two factors equal to 0 to find the two solutions.

Quadratic equations checklist

Remove any fractions by multiplying everything by the lowest common multiple of the denominators.

Multiply out any brackets and collect like terms.

Rewrite in the form $ax^2 + bx + c = 0$

Factorise the left-hand side to solve the quadratic equation.

Now try this

1   Solve $\dfrac{2}{3x-1} - \dfrac{3}{2x+1} = \dfrac{2}{5}$

 Multiply everything by $5(3x - 1)(2x + 1)$ **(5 marks)**

2   Solve $\dfrac{1}{2x+3} - \dfrac{1}{x} = \dfrac{1}{20}$ **(5 marks)**

Using quadratic graphs

You can use graphs to solve quadratic equations. You will need to look for the x-values of the points where a quadratic graph intersects with a straight line.

This grid shows one quadratic graph and two straight-line graphs.

The x-values at A and B are the solutions of the quadratic equation

$$x^2 - 4x = 12$$
or
$$x^2 - 4x - 12 = 0$$

The x-values at C and D are the solutions of the quadratic equation

$$x^2 - 4x = x + 3$$
or
$$x^2 - 5x - 3 = 0$$

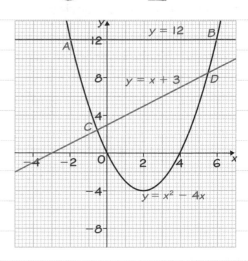

Worked example

This is a graph of $y = 2x^2 + 5x$

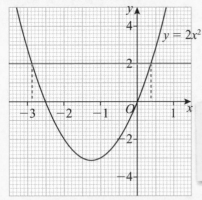

By drawing a suitable straight line on the graph, find estimates for the solutions of the equation $2x^2 + 5x - 2 = 0$

Give your answers correct to 1 decimal place.

(3 marks)

$2x^2 + 5x - 2 = 0$ $(+ 2)$
$\quad 2x^2 + 5x = 2$
$\quad x = 0.4, x = -2.9$

Everything in red is part of the answer.

You can solve the **quadratic equation** $2x^2 + 5x - 2 = 0$ by finding where the graph $y = 2x^2 + 5x$ crosses the straight line $y = 2$

Draw the line $y = 2$ on the graph.

The solutions are the x-values at the points of intersection.

A suitable line

To find a SUITABLE straight line, rearrange the quadratic equation so that the left-hand side matches the equation of the quadratic graph. The right-hand side will tell you which line to draw.
Here is another example:

Graph given: $y = x^2 - 6x + 4$
Equation to solve: $x^2 - 5x + 1 = 0$
Rearrange equation: $x^2 - 6x + 4 = -x + 3$
Line to draw: $y = -x + 3$

Now try this

(a) Complete the table of values for $y = x^2 + 3x - 3$

x	-5	-4	-3	-2	-1	0	1	2
y	7	1			-3	1	7	

(2 marks)

(b) On a grid with $-5 \leqslant x \leqslant 5$ and $-8 \leqslant y \leqslant 8$, draw the graph of $y = x^2 + 3x - 3$ **(2 marks)**

(c) Find estimates for the solutions of $x^2 + 3x - 3 = 0$ **(1 mark)**

(d) By drawing a suitable straight line, work out the solutions of the equation $x^2 + 2x - 4 = 0$ **(3 marks)**

Drawing harder graphs

You can draw any graph using a TABLE OF VALUES. It helps to know the general shape of the graph. Here are two common types of graph you should be able to recognise:

1 Graphs where the highest power is a term in x^3 are called CUBIC GRAPHS.

2 Graphs of the form $y = \dfrac{k}{x}$ are called RECIPROCAL GRAPHS.

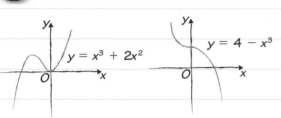

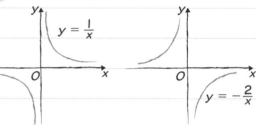

Worked example

Aiming higher

(a) Complete the table of values for $y = x^3 - 4x - 3$

x	-2	-1	0	1	2	3
y	-3	0	-3	-6	-3	12

(2 marks)

(b) On the grid, draw the graph of $y = x^3 - 4x - 3$ for $-2 \leqslant x \leqslant 3$ **(2 marks)**

(c) By drawing a suitable straight line on the grid find an estimate for the solution of the equation
$x^3 - 4x + 3 = 0$ **(3 marks)**

$x^3 - 4x - 9 = 0 \qquad (+ 6)$
$x^3 - 4x - 3 = 6$
Intersection of $y = x^3 - 4x - 3$ and $y = 6$
$x = 2.7$

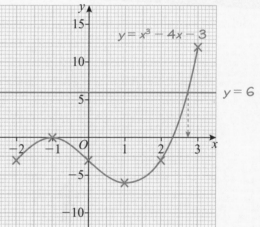

To find a suitable straight line, rearrange the equation so the left-hand side looks like the equation of the graph. There is more about this on page 38.

Now try this

Aiming higher

(a) Complete the table of values for $y = x^2 + \dfrac{1}{x}$
Give values correct to 1 decimal place.

x	0.1	0.2	0.5	1	1.5	2	3	4
y	10.0	5.0		2			9.3	16.3

(2 marks)

(b) On the grid, draw the graph of $y = x^2 + \dfrac{1}{x}$ for $0.1 \leqslant x \leqslant 4$ **(2 marks)**

(c) Use your graph to estimate the solutions of the equation $x^2 + \dfrac{1}{x} = 4$
in the region $0.1 \leqslant x \leqslant 4$ **(3 marks)**

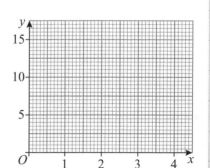

This graph does not have a standard shape. Check that your points follow a smooth curve — if any look wrong, double-check them.

Quadratic inequalities

On page 31 you revised LINEAR INEQUALITIES. In your International GCSE exam, you might need to solve a QUADRATIC INEQUALITY, which involves a SQUARED TERM.

Using a sketch

This graph shows a SKETCH of the CURVE $y = x^2$, and the STRAIGHT LINE $y = 36$

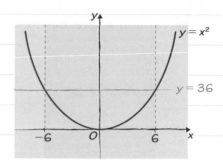

▨ For these values, the curve is BELOW the line, so $x^2 < 36$

The solutions of $x^2 < 36$ are $-6 < x < 6$

▨ For these values, the curve is ABOVE the line, so $x^2 > 36$

The solutions of $x^2 > 36$ are $x < -6$ or $x > 6$

Worked example

Solve the inequality $m^2 \leqslant 25$ **(2 marks)**

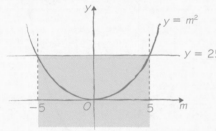

$-5 \leqslant m \leqslant 5$

Draw a sketch of $y = m^2$ and $y = 25$
$\sqrt{25} = 5$ so the graphs intersect at $m = 5$ and $m = -5$
You want m^2 to be **less than or equal to** 25, so you need to consider the values of m between -5 and 5. Make sure you use the same type of inequality signs as those given in the question.

Check it!

Choose a value in your solution range and check it satisfies the original inequality:
$(-3)^2 = 9 \leqslant 25$ ✓

Worked example

Solve the inequality $2x^2 > 18$
Represent your solution on this number line.

(3 marks)

$2x^2 > 18$ $(\div 2)$
$x^2 > 9$

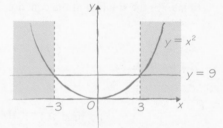

$x > 3$ or $x < -3$

You can divide both sides of any inequality by a **positive number**. So start by dividing both sides by 2. The inequalities are **strict** so represent them with **open circles** on the number line.

Now try this

1 Solve the inequality $p^2 < 4$
Represent your solution on this number line.

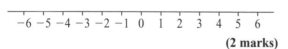

(2 marks)

2 Solve the inequality $3x^2 \geqslant 192$ **(3 marks)**

Start by dividing both sides by 3. Then draw a sketch to work out which values you are interested in.

Simultaneous equations 2

If a pair of simultaneous equations involves an x^2 or a y^2 term, you need to solve them using SUBSTITUTION. Remember to NUMBER the equations to keep track of your working.

Rearrange the linear equation to make y the subject.

$$y = x^2 - 2x - 7 \qquad (1)$$
$$x - y = -3 \qquad (2)$$
$$y = x + 3 \qquad (3)$$

$$x + 3 = x^2 - 2x - 7 \qquad \text{Substitute (3) into (1).}$$
$$0 = x^2 - 3x - 10$$

Each solution for x has a corresponding value of y. Substitute into (3) to find the two solutions.

$$0 = (x - 5)(x + 2)$$
$$x = 5 \text{ or } x = -2$$

The solutions are $x = 5$, $y = 8$ and $x = -2$, $y = 1$

Worked example

Aiming higher

Solve the simultaneous equations

$$x - 2y = 1 \qquad (1)$$
$$x^2 + y^2 = 13 \qquad (2) \qquad \textbf{(6 marks)}$$

$$x = 1 + 2y \qquad (3)$$

Substitute (3) into (2):

$$(1 + 2y)^2 + y^2 = 13$$
$$1 + 4y + 4y^2 + y^2 = 13$$
$$5y^2 + 4y - 12 = 0$$
$$(5y - 6)(y + 2) = 0$$

$$y = \frac{6}{5} \qquad \text{or} \quad y = -2$$
$$x = 1 + 2\left(\frac{6}{5}\right) \qquad x = 1 + 2(-2)$$
$$= \frac{17}{5} \qquad\qquad = -3$$

Solutions: $x = \frac{17}{5}$, $y = \frac{6}{5}$ and
$$x = -3, y = -2$$

EXAM ALERT!

In your exam, simultaneous equations involving y^2 or x^2 will always have **two pairs** of solutions. Each solution is an x-value **and** a y-value. You need to find **four** values in total and pair them up correctly.

Students have struggled with exam questions similar to this – **be prepared!**

You can substitute for x or y. It is easier to substitute for x because there will be no fractions.

Use brackets to make sure that the whole expression is squared.

Rearrange the quadratic equation for y into the form $ay^2 + by + c = 0$

Factorise the left-hand side to find two solutions for y.

Thinking graphically

The solutions to a simultaneous equation correspond to the points where the graphs of each equation INTERSECT. Because an equation involving x^2 or y^2 represents a CURVE, there can be two points of intersection. Each point has an x-value and a y-value. You can write the solutions using coordinates.

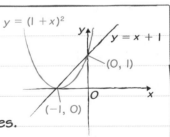

Now try this

Aiming higher

1　Solve the simultaneous equations
$$x - 2y = 3$$
$$x^2 + 2y^2 = 27$$
Show clear algebraic working. **(6 marks)**

2　Solve the simultaneous equations
$$2x = y + 1$$
$$y^2 = 7 + 9x - x^2$$
Show clear algebraic working. **(6 marks)**

Direct proportion

Direct proportion was introduced on page 12. This page looks at it in more detail.

The relationship between the cost of petrol and the number of litres you buy is an example of direct proportion.

If you buy L litres for £C then you can write

- a statement of proportionality: $C \propto L$
  $\propto$ means 'is proportional to'.

- a formula for direct proportion: $C = kL$
  k is called the CONSTANT OF PROPORTIONALITY.

Direct proportion graphs

Straight line. ✓

Passes through the origin. ✓

k is the gradient of the line. ✓

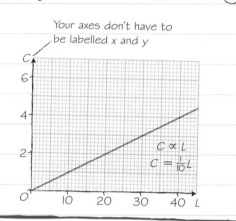

Your axes don't have to be labelled x and y

$C \propto L$
$C = \frac{1}{10}L$

Worked example

Aiming higher

Winnie drops a stone down a well. The speed of the stone, v m/s, is directly proportional to the time, t seconds, since she dropped it.

After 0.5 seconds the stone is travelling at 4.9 m/s.

(a) Find a formula for v in terms of t. **(3 marks)**

$v = kt$
$4.9 = k(0.5) \quad (\div 0.5)$
$k = 9.8$
$v = 9.8t$

(b) Calculate the speed of the stone after 1.2 seconds. **(1 mark)**

$v = 9.8(1.2) = 11.76$ m/s

1. Write down the formula using k for the constant of proportionality.
2. Substitute the values of v and t you are given.
3. Solve the equation to find the value of k.
4. Write down the formula putting in the value of k.
5. Once you have written your formula, you can use it to find the value of one variable if you know the value of the other.

Checking for proportionality

You can use a graph to check whether two quantities are directly proportional.

P	5	10	15
Q	1.2	1.5	1.8

The graph doesn't go through the origin so P and Q are not directly proportional.

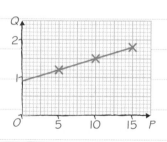

Now try this

x is directly proportional to y.

When $x = 36$, $y = 5$

(a) Find a formula for x in terms of y. **(3 marks)**

(b) Calculate the value of x when $y = 32$ **(1 mark)**

(c) Calculate the value of y when $x = 9$ **(1 mark)**

If two quantities are directly proportional they stay in the same **ratio**.

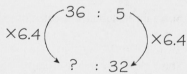

$\times 6.4 \left(\begin{array}{c} 36 : 5 \\ ? : 32 \end{array} \right) \times 6.4$

Proportionality formulae

You can answer some tricky proportionality questions quickly by remembering the proportionality FORMULAE and the shapes of the proportionality GRAPHS.

Proportionality in words	Using $\propto$	Formula
y is directly proportional to x	$y \propto x$	$y = kx$
y is directly proportional to the square of x	$y \propto x^2$	$y = kx^2$
y is directly proportional to the cube of x	$y \propto x^3$	$y = kx^3$
y is directly proportional to the square root of x	$y \propto \sqrt{x}$	$y = k\sqrt{x}$
y is inversely proportional to x	$y \propto \dfrac{1}{x}$	$y = \dfrac{k}{x}$
y is inversely proportional to the square of x	$y \propto \dfrac{1}{x^2}$	$y = \dfrac{k}{x^2}$

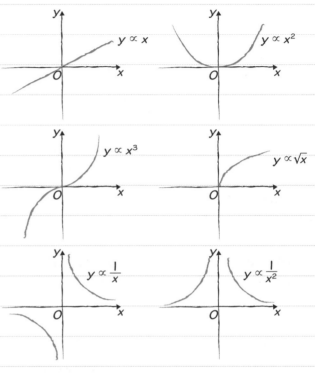

Worked example

Aiming higher

q is <u>inversely proportional</u> to the square of t.

When $t = 4$, $q = 8.5$

Calculate the value of q when $t = 5$ **(5 marks)**

$$q \propto \frac{1}{t^2}$$
$$q = \frac{k}{t^2}$$
$$8.5 = \frac{k}{4^2}$$
$$k = 8.5 \times 4^2 = 136$$
$$q = \frac{136}{t^2}$$
When $t = 5$: $q = \dfrac{136}{5^2} = 5.44$

Always...

1. Write down the statement of proportionality and then the formula.
2. Substitute the values you are given.
3. Solve the equation to find k.
4. Write down the formula using the value of k.
5. Use your formula to find any unknown values.

Don't round your answer unless the question tells you to.

Now try this

Aiming higher

1 v is directly proportional to the cube of z.

     When $z = 12$, $v = 6048$

     (a)   Find a formula for v in terms of z.
                                (3 marks)

     (b)   Calculate the value of v when $z = 18$
                                 (2 marks)

The formula is in the form $v = kz^3$

2   A stone is dropped off a cliff. It takes t seconds to fall a distance d metres.

     t is directly proportional to $\sqrt{d}$

     When $t = 4.6$, $d = 25$

     (a)   Express t in terms of d.   **(3 marks)**

     (b)   Find the length of time the stone takes to fall 42.25 m.   **(2 marks)**

Real-life graphs

You can draw graphs to explain real-life situations. This graph shows the cost of buying some printed T-shirts from three different companies.

Be careful when reading scales on graphs.

Here, 10 small squares represent £50 so each small square represents £5.

Terry's T-shirts would be cheapest if you were ordering 10 T-shirts.

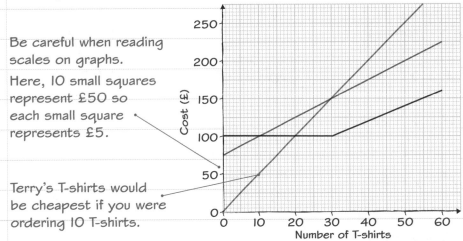

TERRY'S T-SHIRTS
No minimum order
£5 per shirt

SHIRT-O-GRAPH
Set-up cost £75
£2.50 per shirt

PAM'S PRINTING
Special offer up to 30 shirts for £100
Additional shirts just £2

A DISTANCE–TIME graph shows how distance changes with time. This distance–time graph shows Jodi's run. The shape of the graph gives you information about the journey.

A horizontal line means no movement. Jodi rested here for 15 minutes.

The gradient of the graph gives Jodi's speed.

$$\text{Gradient} = \frac{\text{distance in miles}}{\text{time in hours}} = 1.9 \div \frac{1}{2} = 3.8$$

Jodi was travelling at 3.8 mph on this section of the run.

This is when Jodi turned around and started heading back home.

The horizontal scale might be marked in minutes or hours. Remember that there are 60 minutes in 1 hour.

Straight lines mean that Jodi was travelling at a constant speed.

At 13:15 Jodi was 1.4 miles from home.

Jodi sped up when she was nearly home. The graph is steeper here.

Now try this

Beth leaves home in her car at 09:30 and returns at 11:45.

The graph shows her journey.

(a) How far does she travel altogether? **(1 mark)**

(b) For how long does the car stop altogether?

(2 marks)

(c) Work out the speed of the car on the fastest part of the journey. **(3 marks)**

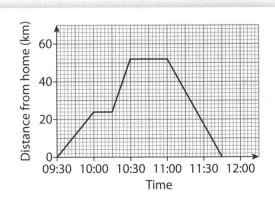

Sequences

An ARITHMETIC SEQUENCE is a sequence of numbers where the difference between consecutive terms is CONSTANT. In your exam, you might need to work out the nth term of a sequence. Look at this example which shows you how to do it in four steps.

 Here is a sequence.

1 $\boxed{+4}$ 5 $\boxed{+4}$ 9 $\boxed{+4}$ 13 $\boxed{+4}$ 17

Work out a formula for the nth term of the sequence.
(2 marks)

> Write in the difference between each term.

 Here is a sequence.

Zero term
−3   1 $\boxed{+4}$ 5 $\boxed{+4}$ 9 $\boxed{+4}$ 13 $\boxed{+4}$ 17

Work out a formula for the nth term of the sequence.
(2 marks)

> Work backwards to find the **zero term** of the sequence. You need to subtract 4 from the first term.

 Here is a sequence.

Zero term
−3   1 $\boxed{+4}$ 5 $\boxed{+4}$ 9 $\boxed{+4}$ 13 $\boxed{+4}$ 17

Work out a formula for the nth term of the sequence.
(2 marks)

nth term = difference × n + zero term

> Write down the formula for the nth term.
> **Remember** this formula for the exam.

 Here is a sequence.

Zero term
−3   1 $\boxed{+4}$ 5 $\boxed{+4}$ 9 $\boxed{+4}$ 13 $\boxed{+4}$ 17

Work out a formula for the nth term of the sequence.
(2 marks)

nth term = difference × n + zero term
nth term = $4n - 3$

Is 99 in this sequence?

You can use the nth term to check whether a number is a term in the sequence.

The value of n in your nth term has to be a POSITIVE whole number.

Try some different values of n:

$n = 25 \rightarrow 4n - 3 = 97$

$n = 26 \rightarrow 4n - 3 = 101$

You can't use a value of n between 25 and 26 so 99 is NOT a term in the sequence.

Check it!

Check your answer by substituting values of n into your nth term.

1st term: when $n = 1$,
$4n - 3 = 4 \times 1 - 3 = 1$
2nd term: when $n = 2$,
$4n - 3 = 4 \times 2 - 3 = 5$ ✓

You can also generate any term of the sequence.

For the 20th term, $n = 20$:

$4n - 3 = 4 \times 20 - 3 = 77$

So the 20th term is 77.

Now try this

Here is a sequence: 2   5   8   11   14   ……

(a) Work out an expression for the nth term of the sequence.   **(2 marks)**

(b) Work out the 29th term in the sequence.   **(2 marks)**

(c) How many terms of this sequence are **less than** 200?   **(2 marks)**

(d) Is 156 a term in this sequence?   **(2 marks)**

Functions

A function maps numbers in its DOMAIN onto numbers in its RANGE. Here is an example:

f is the NAME of the function. You can use any letter, but f and g are the most common.

$$f(x) = \sqrt{x - 2} \qquad x \geqslant 2$$

This is the DOMAIN of the function. The function is only defined for these INPUT values. The RANGE of this function is $f(x) \geqslant 0$. This tells you all the possible OUTPUT values for the function.

x is the INPUT. You say "f of x". You can also write $f : x \rightarrow \sqrt{x - 2}$ and say "f maps x onto $\sqrt{x - 2}$"

This tells you what the function does to x.

Worked example

f is the function $f(x) = 3x + 10$

(a) Find $f(-2)$ **(1 mark)**

$f(-2) = 3 \times (-2) + 10$
$= -6 + 10 = 4$

(b) Solve $f(a) = 31$ **(2 marks)**

$3a + 10 = 31 \qquad (-10)$
$3a = 21 \qquad (\div 3)$
$a = 7$

If the question doesn't ask you about the **domain** or the **range** then you don't need to worry about them.

(a) To find $f(-2)$ you just **substitute** $x = -2$ into the expression for $f(x)$

(b) Substitute $x = a$ into the expression for $f(x)$ then solve the equation to find a.

Excluding values

A function must be clearly defined. EVERY VALUE in the DOMAIN can be used as an input. This means that you sometimes have to EXCLUDE values from the domain. Here are two cases to learn:

1 You can't DIVIDE BY 0

$f(x) = \dfrac{x}{x - 2} \qquad x \neq 2$

You have to exclude $x = 2$ from the domain.

2 You can't SQUARE ROOT a NEGATIVE NUMBER

$g(x) = \sqrt{+3} \qquad x \geqslant -3$

You have to exclude values of x less than -3

Worked example

Aiming higher

The function f is defined as
$f(x) = \dfrac{1}{x + 7}$

(a) Find the value of $f(3)$ **(1 mark)**

$f(3) = \dfrac{1}{3 + 7} = \dfrac{1}{10}$

(b) State which value(s) of x must be excluded from the domain of f. **(1 mark)**

$x = -7$

For part (b), work out what the possible **output** values could be if the input values are $x \geqslant 2$

Write your answer as $f(x) \geqslant \square$

Now try this

1 The function f is defined as $f(x) = \dfrac{x + 3}{x}$

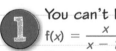

(a) Find $f(1)$ **(1 mark)**

(b) State which value of x cannot be included in the domain of f. **(1 mark)**

(c) Given that $f(b) = 3$, find the value of b. **(2 marks)**

2 $f(x) = (x + 1)^2$

(a) Find $f(3)$ **(1 mark)**

(b) The domain of f is all values of x where $x \geqslant 2$ Find the range of f. **(2 marks)**

$g(x) = \sqrt{x - 5}$

(c) Which values of x cannot be included in the domain of g? **(2 marks)**

Composite functions

If you apply two functions one after the other, you can write a SINGLE FUNCTION which has the same effect as the two combined functions. This is called a COMPOSITE FUNCTION.

The function gf has the same effect as applying function f THEN applying function g.

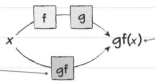

The ORDER is important. The function being applied FIRST goes CLOSEST to the x.

Order is important in composite functions. You can think of fg(x) as f[g(x)]
You work out g(x) **first**, then you use this answer as your **input** for f(x)
Note that in this case gf(10) would give you a **different answer**:

$$f(10) = 10^2 = 100$$
$$g(100) = 100 - 3 = 97$$
So gf(10) = 97

Worked example   *Aiming higher*

$f(x) = x^2$
$g(x) = x - 3$
Find fg(10)   **(2 marks)**

$g(10) = 10 - 3 = 7$
$f(7) = 7^2 = 49$
So fg(10) = 49

Worked example

Aiming higher

$f(x) = 3x + 2$
$g(x) = \dfrac{x}{x + 2}$
Find fg(x)

Give your answer as a single algebraic fraction expressed as simply as possible.   **(3 marks)**

$fg(x) = f[g(x)] = f\left[\dfrac{x}{x+2}\right]$

$= 3\left[\dfrac{x}{x+2}\right] + 2$

$= \dfrac{3x}{x+2} + 2$

$= \dfrac{3x}{x+2} + \dfrac{2(x+2)}{x+2}$

$= \dfrac{3x + 2x + 4}{x+2} = \dfrac{5x+4}{x+2}$

Finding fg(x)

To find an algebraic expression for fg(x) you need to:

 Write fg(x) as f[g(x)]

 Substitute the WHOLE EXPRESSION for g(x) for each instance of x in the expression for f(x)
Use square brackets when you substitute.

 Simplify the new expression as much as possible.
You might have to expand brackets or simplify algebraic fractions.

Now try this

Aiming higher

1 The functions f and g are such that
$f(x) = 2x - 2$ and $g(x) = x^2 - 4$

(a) Find gf(x)
Give your answer as simply as possible.
(2 marks)

(b) Solve gf(x) = 0   **(3 marks)**

In part (a), remember to substitute $(x + 1)$ for **both** instances of x in the expression for g(x)

2 $f(x) = x + 1$
$g(x) = \dfrac{x}{2x - 1}$

(a) Find gf(x)
Give your answer as simply as possible.
(2 marks)

(b) Find fg(x)
Give your answer as a single algebraic fraction expressed as simply as possible.   **(3 marks)**

Inverse functions

For a function f, the INVERSE of f is the function that UNDOES f. You write the inverse as f^{-1}. If you apply f then f^{-1}, you will end up back where you started.

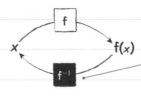

If you apply f, then f^{-1} you have applied the COMPOSITE FUNCTION $f^{-1}f$. The output of $f^{-1}f$ is the SAME as the input. You can write:

$$f^{-1}f(x) = ff^{-1}(x) = x$$

Finding the inverse

To find the inverse of a function given in the form f(x) = ... you need to:

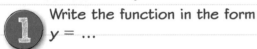 Write the function in the form $y = ...$

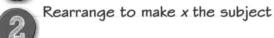 Rearrange to make x the subject

 Swap any y's for x's and rewrite as $f^{-1}(x) = ...$

For a reminder on changing the subject of a formula, have a look at page 30.

Worked example

$g(x) = \dfrac{3}{x + 4}$

Express the inverse function g^{-1} in the form $g^{-1}(x) = ...$ **(3 marks)**

$$y = \frac{3}{x + 4} \quad (\times (x + 4))$$
$$y(x + 4) = 3 \quad (\div y)$$
$$x + 4 = \frac{3}{y} \quad (- 4)$$
$$x = \frac{3}{y} - 4 \quad \text{(Swap y's for x's)}$$
$$g^{-1}(x) = \frac{3}{x} - 4$$

Start by multiplying both sides by (x + 4). You want x on its own on the left-hand side so don't expand the bracket. Once you've rearranged to make x the subject, swap any y's for x's and and write your answer as $g^{-1}(x) = ...$

Worked example

f is the function f(x) = 3x + 5

Express the inverse function f^{-1} in the form $f^{-1}(x) = ...$ **(2 marks)**

$$y = 3x + 5 \quad (- 5)$$
$$y - 5 = 3x \quad (\div 3)$$
$$\frac{y - 5}{3} = x \quad \text{(Swap y's for x's)}$$
$$f^{-1}(x) = \frac{x - 5}{3}$$

You can also use a flow chart to find an inverse.
Here is a flow chart for f(x)

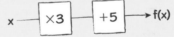

You work **backwards** through the flow chart to find $f^{-1}(x)$

$f^{-1}(x) \leftarrow \boxed{\div 3} \boxed{-5} \leftarrow x$

You subtract 5, **then** divide by 3. Written using algebra this is

$$f^{-1}(x) = \frac{x - 5}{3}$$

Now try this

 Aiming higher

1 f is the function f(x) = 2x − 1
   (a) Express the inverse function f^{-1} in the form $f^{-1}(x) = ...$ **(2 marks)**
   (b) Without doing any further working, write down the value of $f^{-1}f(7)$ **(1 mark)**

2 The function g is such that $g : x \to \dfrac{x + 6}{x}$
   Express the inverse function g^{-1} in the form $g^{-1} : x \to ...$ **(3 marks)**

Group all the terms involving x on one side, then factorise to get x on its own.

Functions and graphs

You can use graphs of the form $y = f(x)$ or $y = g(x)$ to represent functions. The y coordinates on the graph tell you the OUTPUT values of the function for given values of x.

Worked example

The diagram shows part of the graph of $y = f(x)$ and part of the graph of $y = g(x)$

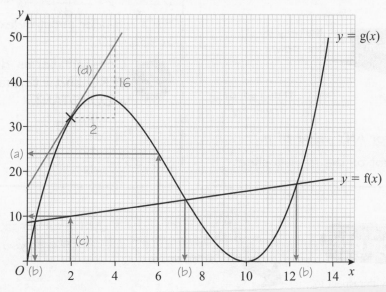

(a) Find the value of g(6)   **(1 mark)**

$g(6) = 24$

(b) Solve the equation $f(x) = g(x)$
                                          (2 marks)

$x = 0.4$, $x = 7.2$, $x = 12.3$

(c) Find gf(2)   **(2 marks)**

$f(2) = 10$, $g(10) = 0$

So $gf(2) = 0$

(d) Find an estimate for the gradient of the graph of $y = g(x)$ at the point (2, 32)   **(3 marks)**

$\text{Gradient} = \dfrac{\text{vertical difference}}{\text{horizontal difference}}$

$= \dfrac{48 - 32}{4 - 2}$

$= \dfrac{16}{2} = 8$

(a) Read up from $x = 6$ to the graph of $y = g(x)$, then read across to the y-axis.

(b) The solutions are the x-values at the points where the graphs intersect.

(c) To work out gf(x) you find f(x) first, then use that as your input for g(x)

There is more about composite functions on page 47.

(d) You can **estimate** the gradient of a curve by drawing a **tangent**. Use a ruler to draw a straight line that **just touches** the curve at the given point. Then work out the gradient of your straight line using

$\dfrac{\text{vertical difference}}{\text{horizontal difference}}$

Make sure you use the **scale** on the graph — don't just count grid squares.

Now try this

Look at the diagram in the worked example above.

Aiming higher

(a) Find g(8)   **(1 mark)**

(b) Find fg(12)   **(2 marks)**

(c) Find an estimate for the gradient of the graph $y = g(x)$ at the point (8, 8)   **(3 marks)**

Differentiation

You can DIFFERENTIATE a function to find its DERIVATIVE or GRADIENT FUNCTION, $\frac{dy}{dx}$

Differentiating x^n

In your International GCSE exam all the functions you have to differentiate will have terms of the form ax^n.

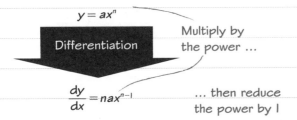

$$y = ax^n$$

Differentiation → Multiply by the power ...

$$\frac{dy}{dx} = nax^{n-1}$$ ... then reduce the power by 1

This rule works for ANY value of n.

Learn this — it's not on the formula sheet.

Golden rules

1 Write every term in the form ax^n before differentiating.

$$y = \frac{1}{x} = x^{-1} \rightarrow \frac{dy}{dx} = -x^{-2}$$

For a reminder about index laws have a look at page 20.

2 Constant terms differentiate to ZERO and x terms differentiate to a CONSTANT.

$$y = 9x \rightarrow \frac{dy}{dx} = 9$$

$$y = 25 \rightarrow \frac{dy}{dx} = 0$$

Worked example

"With respect to x" just means that x is the variable. If there were any other letters, you would treat them as **constants**.

Differentiate with respect to x:

(a) $5x^2$ **(1 mark)**

$$y = 5x^2$$
$$\frac{dy}{dx} = 10x$$

(b) $\frac{3}{x}$ **(2 marks)**

$$y = \frac{3}{x} = 3x^{-1}$$
$$\frac{dy}{dx} = -3x^{-2}$$

(a) You multiply by the power, then reduce the power by 1.
$$\frac{dy}{dx} = 2 \times 5x^{2-1} = 10x$$

(b) You need every term to be in the form ax^n before you differentiate. Start by rewriting $\frac{3}{x}$ as $3x^{-1}$. Then multiply by the power and reduce the power by 1:
$$\frac{dy}{dx} = -1 \times 3x^{-1-1} = -3x^{-2} \text{ or } \frac{-3}{x^2}$$

Differentiate **term by term**. Be careful with the signs. Remember that the x term gives a **constant** so differentiating $-6x$ gives -6. Any constant terms go to **zero**, so the $+10$ term disappears when you differentiate.

Worked example

For the curve with equation $y = 2x^3 - 6x + 10$, find $\frac{dy}{dx}$ **(2 marks)**

$$y = 2x^3 - 6x + 10$$
$$\frac{dy}{dx} = 6x^2 - 6$$

Now try this

1 Differentiate with respect to x

(a) $4x^2 + 6x - 1$ **(2 marks)**

(b) $\frac{2}{x}$ **(2 marks)**

2 (a) Write $\frac{1 + x}{x^2}$ in the form $x^a + x^b$ where a and b are integers. **(2 marks)**

(b) Differentiate $\frac{1 + x}{x^2}$ with respect to x. **(2 marks)**

Finding gradients

You can use the DERIVATIVE or GRADIENT FUNCTION to find the RATE OF CHANGE of a function, or the gradient of a curve.

This curve has equation $y = x^3 + 5x^2$. Its gradient function has equation $\dfrac{dy}{dx} = 3x^2 + 10x$. You can find the GRADIENT at any point on the graph by substituting the x-coordinate at that point into the gradient function.

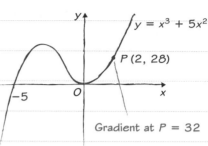

$y = x^3 + 5x^2$

$P\,(2, 28)$

-5

Gradient at $P = 32$

At the point P, $x = 2$, so $\dfrac{dy}{dx} = 3(2)^2 + 10(2) = 12 + 20 = 32$ The gradient at P is 32.

Worked example — Aiming higher

For the curve with equation $y = x^3 - 5x + 7$

(a) find $\dfrac{dy}{dx}$ **(2 marks)**

$y = x^3 - 5x + 7$

$\dfrac{dy}{dx} = 3x^2 - 5$

(b) find the gradient of the curve at the point where $x = 5$ **(2 marks)**

When $x = 5$, $\dfrac{dy}{dx} = 3(5)^2 - 5$

$= 75 - 5 = 70$

(a) Differentiate **term-by-term** to find $\dfrac{dy}{dx}$
For a reminder about differentiating have a look at page 50.

(b) The value of $\dfrac{dy}{dx}$ when $x = 5$ tells you the **gradient** of the **original curve** when $x = 5$. Substitute $x = 5$ into the expression for $\dfrac{dy}{dx}$

EXAM ALERT!

In this question you are given the **gradient** and you have to find the **coordinates** of the points with that gradient. Follow these steps:

1. Differentiate to find the gradient function.

2. Set the gradient function equal to 48.

3. **Solve** the equation to find the values of x with that gradient.

   Be careful — there may be more than one solution.

4. Substitute those values of x into the **original** equation to find the corresponding values of y.

Students have struggled with exam questions similar to this – **be prepared!**

Worked example — Aiming higher

Find the coordinates of the points on the curve $y = x^3$ where the gradient is 48.   **(3 marks)**

$y = x^3$

$\dfrac{dy}{dx} = 3x^2$

When $\dfrac{dy}{dx} = 48$, $3x^2 = 48$ $(\div 3)$

$x^2 = 16$ $(\sqrt{\,})$

$x = 4$ or $x = -4$

If $x = 4$, $y = 4^3 = 64$

If $x = -4$, $y = (-4)^3 = -64$

The two points are $(4, 64)$ and $(-4, -64)$

Now try this

Aiming higher

1 For the curve with equation $y = 3x^3 + 2x^2 + 5$

   (a) find $\dfrac{dy}{dx}$ **(2 marks)**

   (b) find the gradient of the curve at the point where $x = 2$ **(2 marks)**

2 Find the coordinates of the point on the curve $y = 5x^2 + 3x + 2$ where the gradient is 11

   (3 marks)

Aiming higher

3 For the curve with equation $2x^3 - 6x + 1$

   (a) find $\dfrac{dy}{dx}$ **(2 marks)**

   (b) find the coordinates of the two points on the curve where the gradient of the curve is 0

   (4 marks)

Set $\dfrac{dy}{dx} = 0$ to find **two** values of x.

Turning points

You can use DIFFERENTIATION to find the TURNING POINT of a GRAPH or FUNCTION in your International GCSE exam. You need to be confident with differentiation so revise that on pages 50 and 51 first.

Golden rule

The turning points of a graph or function are the points where the DERIVATIVE,

or GRADIENT FUNCTION, $\frac{dy}{dx}$, is equal to ZERO.

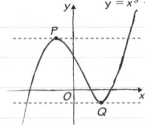

$y = x^3 - 5x + 3$

This graph has turning points at P and Q. The gradient is 0 at both points.

Worked example

Find the coordinates of the turning point on the curve with equation $y = 3x^2 + 12x + 5$ **(4 marks)**

$$\frac{dy}{dx} = 6x + 12$$

When $\frac{dy}{dx} = 0$, $6x + 12 = 0$

$6x = -12$

$x = -2$

So $y = 3 \times (-2)^2 + 12 \times (-2) + 5 = -7$

Turning point is $(-2, -7)$

To find the coordinates of the turning point using differentiation:

1. Differentiate to find $\frac{dy}{dx}$
2. Set $\frac{dy}{dx} = 0$
3. Solve the equation to find the value or values of x.
4. Find the corresponding value of y for each value of x.

Maximum or minimum?

For a QUADRATIC function, the turning point is either a maximum or a minimum. You can work out which using the COEFFICIENT of x^2.

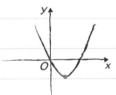

If the coefficient of x^2 is POSITIVE the turning point is a MINIMUM.

If the coefficient of x^2 is NEGATIVE the turning point is a MAXIMUM.

Worked example

For $A = 6x^2 - 90x + 10$

(a) find $\frac{dA}{dx}$ **(2 marks)**

$$\frac{dA}{dx} = 12x - 90$$

(b) find the value of x for which A is a minimum.   **(2 marks)**

When $\frac{dA}{dx} = 0$, $12x - 90 = 0$ $(+ 90)$

$12x = 90$ $(\div 12)$

$x = 7.5$

(c) explain how you know that A is a minimum for this value of x.   **(1 mark)**

Because the coefficient of x^2 is positive.

Now try this

Aiming higher

1 (a) Find the coordinates of the turning point on the curve with equation $y = x^2 - 8x + 3$
    (4 marks)

(b) State with a reason whether this turning point is a minimum or a maximum.   **(1 mark)**

2 For the curve with equation $y = x^3 - 5x^2 + 8x + 1$

(a) find $\frac{dy}{dx}$ **(2 marks)**

(b) find the x-coordinates of the two turning points on the curve.   **(4 marks)**

Kinematics

Kinematics deals with the MOTION of objects. You can use DIFFERENTIATION to solve problems involving the DISPLACEMENT, VELOCITY and ACCELERATION of an object.

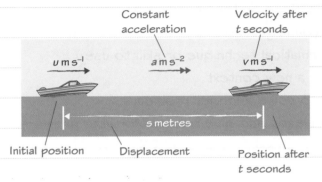

Worked example

A particle moves in a straight line through a fixed point O. The displacement of the particle from O at time t seconds is s metres, where
$$s = t^2 - 6t + 10$$

(a) Find $\dfrac{ds}{dt}$ (2 marks)

$$\frac{ds}{dt} = 2t - 6$$

(b) Find the velocity of particle when $t = 5$ (2 marks)

$$v = \frac{ds}{dt} = 2t - 6$$
When $t = 5$, $v = 2(5) - 6$
$$= 10 - 6$$
$$= 4 \text{ m/s}$$

(c) Find the acceleration of the particle.   (2 marks)

$$v = 2t - 6$$
$$a = \frac{dv}{dt} = 2 \text{ m/s}^2$$

Differentiating with respect to time

The derivative tells you the RATE OF CHANGE of one variable with respect to another.

Displacement, s

Differentiation

Velocity, v = rate of change of displacement with time = $\dfrac{ds}{dt}$

Differentiation

Acceleration, a = rate of change of velocity with time = $\dfrac{dv}{dt}$

Differentiate the expression for s once to find an expression for v. The units for velocity are metres per second (m/s). Differentiate again to find an expression for a. The units for acceleration are metres per second per second (m/s^2).

Set $\dfrac{ds}{dt} = 0$ and solve to find the value of t which gives a **maximum** value of s. Then substitute this value of t back into the equation for s to find the maximum height.

Now try this

Aiming higher

A stone is projected vertically upwards from the ground. After t seconds its height above the ground, s metres, is given by
$$s = 15t - 4.9t^2 \quad \text{for } 0 \leq t \leq 4$$

(a) Find $\dfrac{ds}{dt}$ (2 marks)

(b) Find the velocity of the stone when $t = 0.5$ (1 mark)

(c) Find the maximum height of the stone above the ground, correct to 1 decimal place.   (3 marks)

Problem-solving practice

Problem-solving skills are essential to success in your International GCSE exam.
Practise using the questions on the next two pages.
For these questions you might need to:

* choose which mathematical technique or skill to use
* apply a technique in a new context
* plan your strategy to solve a longer problem
* show your working clearly and give reasons for your answers.

1

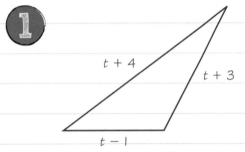

The perimeter of this triangle is 19 cm.
All lengths on the diagram are in cm.
Work out the value of t.   (4 marks)

Linear equations 2 p. 29

Use the information in the question to write an equation. Solve your equation to work out the value of t.

TOP TIP

Remember to simplify your equation by collecting like terms before solving.

2 The diagram shows a line ABCD.
A is the point (30, 18)
B is the point (18, 12)
The line cuts the y-axis at C and the x-axis at D.

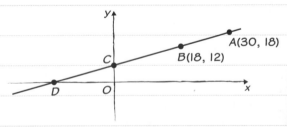

Work out the coordinates of C and D.
(4 marks)

Straight-line graphs p. 25

You need to find the equation of the line. Draw a right-angled triangle with AB as its longest side to find the gradient. Then substitute the x and y values at one of the points into $y = mx + c$ and solve the equation to find c. Remember that the x- and y-values for any point on a line satisfy the equation of the line.

TOP TIP

When you are solving straight-line graph problems you might need to substitute values into $y = mx + c$ and solve an equation to find the gradient or the y-intercept.

Problem-solving practice

 3 Factorise completely
$(6a + b)^2 - (a - 3b)^2$

(2 marks)

Factorising p. 22

This is in the form $x^2 - y^2$ with $x = 6a + b$ and $y = a - 3b$

Use this rule:

$(x + y)(x - y) = x^2 - y^2$

TOP TIP

If you have to factorise an expression, always keep an eye out for the difference of two squares.

---

 4 (a) Show that $\dfrac{x^2 - 2x}{3x^2 - 5x - 2}$ can be written as $\dfrac{x}{kx + 1}$ and state the value of k. (3 marks)

(b) $f(x) = \dfrac{x}{3x + 1}$

Find the inverse function f^{-1} in the form $f^{-1}(x) = ...$, showing your working clearly.

(3 marks)

Algebraic fractions p. 23 Inverse functions p. 48

In part (a), you need to **factorise** the top and bottom of the fraction before cancelling one of the factors.

TOP TIP

Finding an inverse of a function is the same skill as **rearranging formulae**. Check you are confident with that on page 30.

---

5 At an open-air sale, two plots are marked out using tape. *ABFE* is a rectangle of width x m and length y m. The line *CD* divides it into two equal parts. The total length of tape used is 60 m.

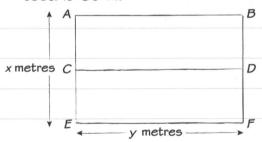

(a) (i) Show that $y = 20 - \dfrac{2}{3}x$

The area of the rectangle *ABFE* is A m^2

(ii) Show that $A = 20x - \dfrac{2}{3}x^2$ (3 marks)

(b) Find $\dfrac{dA}{dx}$ (2 marks)

(c) Find the maximum value of A. (3 marks)

Differentiation p. 50 Turning points p. 52

(a) You are given the length of tape used. The diagram shows you that you need 3 lots of y m and 2 lots of x m. Use this information to write down the relationship between x and y using algebra, then rearrange your equation until it matches the one given.

(b) When you differentiate, the variables don't have to be y and x. Here they are A and x.

(c) The maximum value for A occurs at the **turning point**. Set $\dfrac{dA}{dx}$ equal to 0 and solve an equation to find A.

TOP TIP

If you get stuck on an early part of a long question, see if you have enough information to tackle a later part. In this question you could do part (b) even if you haven't completed part (a).

Angle properties

You need to remember all of these angle properties and their correct names.

CORRESPONDING
ANGLES are equal.

ALTERNATE ANGLES
are equal.

ALLIED ANGLES
(or INTERIOR ANGLES)
add up to 180°.

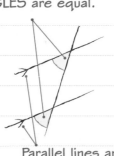

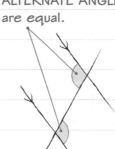

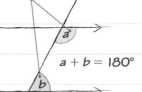

$a + b = 180°$

Parallel lines are
marked with arrows.

VERTICALLY OPPOSITE ANGLES
are equal.

These are useful angle facts for triangles
and parallelograms:

Interior
angle

The exterior angle of a
triangle is equal to the
sum of the interior angles
at the other two vertices.

Exterior
angle

$a + b$

The opposite
angles of a
parallelogram
are equal.

You need to know the proofs of the angle
properties of triangles and quadrilaterals.

Golden rule

When answering angle problems, you
need to give a reason for each step of
your working.

Angle sums

You need to remember these two angle
facts:

1 The angles in a triangle add up to
180°

2 The angles in a quadrilateral add
up to 360°

Worked example

Use the fact that the angles in a triangle add
up to 180° to write an equation, then solve
your equation to find x. For a reminder about
solving linear equations have a look at p. 28.

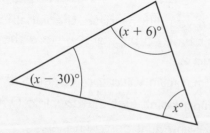

$(x + 6)°$

$(x - 30)°$

$x°$

Work out the value of x.   **(3 marks)**

Angles in a triangle add up to 180° so

$(x - 30) + (x + 6) + x = 180$

$3x - 24 = 180$ $(+ 24)$

$3x = 204$ $(÷ 3)$

$x = 68$

Now try this

AB is parallel to CD.

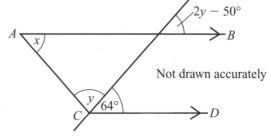

$2y - 50°$

A x B

Not drawn accurately

y $64°$

C D

Work out the value of x.   **(5 marks)**

Solving angle problems

You might need to use angle properties to solve problems in your exam. Remember to give reasons for every step of your working.

Reasons

Use these reasons in angle problems:
- Angles on a straight line add up to 180°.
- Angles around a point add up to 360°.
- Opposite angles are equal.
- Corresponding angles are equal.
- Alternate angles are equal.
- Angles in a triangle add up to 180°.
- Angles in a quadrilateral add up to 360°.
- Base angles of an isosceles triangle are equal.

Use the properties on the diagram:
AB is parallel to CD
AC is parallel to BD
BE is equal to DE

Worked example

Work out the size of the angle marked x.
Give reasons for each step of your working.

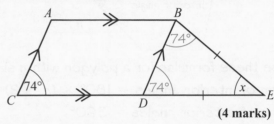

(4 marks)

$\angle BDE = 74°$ (corresponding angles are equal)

$\angle DBE = 74°$ (base angles in an isosceles triangle are equal)

$x + 74° + 74° = 180°$ (angles in a triangle add up to 180°)

$x = 180° - 148°$

$x = 32°$

Worked example

ABCD is a quadrilateral.

Angle *DAB* is a right angle.

Angles *ABC* and *BCD* are in the ratio 1 : 2

Angle *CDA* is 70° more than angle *ABC*.

Work out the size of angles *ABC*, *BCD* and *CDA*.

(4 marks)

$A = 90°$
$C = 2x$
$D = x + 70°$
$A + B + C + D = 360°$ (angles in a quadrilateral add up to 360°)
So $90° + x + 2x + (x + 70°) = 360°$
$\qquad\qquad 4x = 200°$
$\qquad\qquad x = 50°$
So $B = 50°$, $C = 2 \times 50° = 100°$ and $D = 50° + 70° = 120°$

Write angle *B* as *x* then express angles *C* and *D* in terms of *x*.
Angle problems could involve ratio or proportion, or you might need to write your own equation.

Now try this

In the diagram *ABC* and *BDC* are isosceles triangles.

Express the size of angle *ABD* in terms of *x*, giving your answer as simply as possible.

Give a reason for each step of your working.

(4 marks)

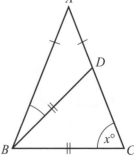

Angles in polygons

Polygon questions are all about interior and exterior angles.

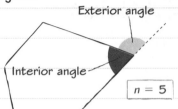

Exterior angle

Interior angle

$n = 5$

Use these formulae for a polygon with n sides.

Sum of interior angles $= 180° \times (n - 2)$

Sum of exterior angles $= 360°$

This diagram shows part of a REGULAR polygon with 30 sides.

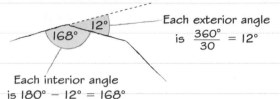

168° 12°

Each exterior angle is $\frac{360°}{30} = 12°$

Each interior angle is $180° - 12° = 168°$

Don't try to draw a 30-sided polygon!

If there's no diagram given in a polygon question, you probably don't need to draw one.

Regular polygons

In a regular polygon all the sides are equal and all the angles are equal.

If a regular polygon has n sides then each exterior angle is $\frac{360°}{n}$

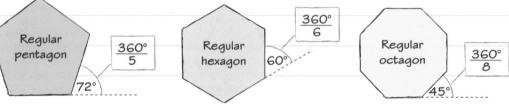

Regular pentagon $\frac{360°}{5}$ 72°

Regular hexagon 60° $\frac{360°}{6}$

Regular octagon $\frac{360°}{8}$ 45°

You can use the fact that the angles on a straight line add up to 180° to work out the size of one of the interior angles.

Worked example

Diagram **NOT** accurately drawn

The diagram shows part of a regular polygon.
The interior angle and the exterior angle at a vertex are marked.
The size of the interior angle is 7 times the size of the exterior angle.
Work out the number of sides of the polygon. **(3 marks)**

$180° \div 8 = 22.5°$

$\frac{360°}{22.5°} = 16$

The polygon has 16 sides.

The ratio of the interior angle to the exterior angle is 7 : 1
Because these are angles on a straight line they add up to 180°, so divide 180° in the ratio 7 : 1

There is more on dividing a quantity in a given ratio on page 11.

It is usually easier to work with **exterior angles** in polygon questions. You can rearrange the formula for the size of an exterior angle to get:

$n = \frac{360°}{\text{exterior angle}}$

Now try this

The diagram shows part of a regular polygon.
Work out the number of sides in the polygon. **(3 marks)**

156°

Circle facts

You need to know the names of the different parts of a circle.

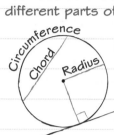

Diameter = radius × 2

Tangent

The other parts of a circle are shown on pages 64 and 83.

When you are solving circle problems:

- correctly identify the angle to be found
- use all the information given in the question
- mark all calculated angles on the diagram
- give a reason for each step of your working.

You might need to use angle facts about triangles, quadrilaterals and parallel lines in circle questions. There is a list of angle facts on page 57.

Key circle facts

 The angle between a radius and a tangent is 90°.

 Two tangents which meet at a point outside a circle are the same length.

3 A triangle which has one vertex at the centre of a circle and two vertices on the circumference is an ISOSCELES TRIANGLE.

Each short side of the triangle is a radius, so they are the same length.

Remember that the base angles of an isosceles triangle are equal.

Worked example

A and *B* are points on the circumference of a circle centre *O*.
AC and *BC* are both tangents to the circle. Angle *BCA* = 42°
Work out the size of the angle marked *x*.   **(3 marks)**

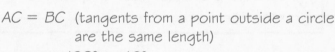

$AC = BC$ (tangents from a point outside a circle are the same length)

$\angle ABC = \dfrac{180° - 42°}{2} = 69°$

(base angles in an isosceles △ are equal, and angles in a △ add up to 180°)

$x + 69° = 90°$ (angle between a tangent and a radius = 90°)

$x = 21°$

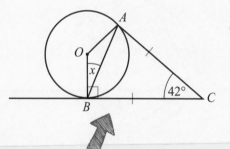

$AC = BC$, so mark these lines with a dash. Make sure you write down the circle fact you are using as well. To write a really good answer you have to give a reason for each step of your working.

Now try this

A, *B* and *C* are points on the circumference of a circle with centre *O*. *CD* is a tangent to the circle. Angle *AOB* = 53°
Work out the size of angle *BCD*.   **(3 marks)**

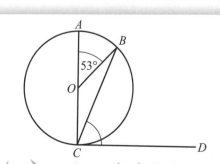

Make sure you write down every step of your working.

Circle theorems

If you're aiming for an A or A* you need to LEARN these six circle theorems.

 The perpendicular from a chord to the centre of the circle bisects the chord.

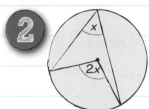 The angle at the centre of the circle is twice the angle on the circumference.

 The angle in a semicircle is 90°.

 Angles in the same segment are equal.

 Opposite angles of a cyclic quadrilateral add up to 180°.

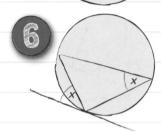 The angle between a tangent and a chord is equal to the angle in the alternate segment.

This is called the ALTERNATE SEGMENT THEOREM.

See page 59 for more circle facts.

Circle theorem top tips

☑ If you can spot a tangent and a chord in your circle then you might be able to use the ALTERNATE SEGMENT THEOREM.

☑ WRITE the unknown angles on your diagram as you go.

☑ Give REASONS for each step of your working.

Worked example

Aiming higher

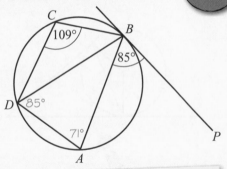

Everything in red is part of the answer.

You might need to use other angle facts in a circle theorem question. Look at page 57 for a reminder.

Angle *ABP* = 85° and angle *BCD* = 109°

Calculate the size of angle *ABD*.

Give reasons for each step of your working.

(4 marks)

$\angle ADB = 85°$ (alternate segment theorem)

$180 - 109 = 71$

$\angle DAB = 71°$ (opposite angles in a cyclic quadrilateral add up to 180°)

$180 - 85 - 71 = 24$

$\angle ABD = 24°$ (angles in a triangle add up to 180°)

Now try this

Aiming higher

ABCD is a cyclic quadrilateral.

PBQ is a tangent to the circle at *B*.

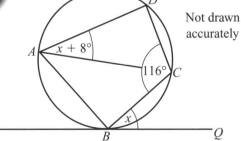

Not drawn accurately

Work out the value of *x*.   **(4 marks)**

Intersecting chords

You need to know these rules about intersecting chords in the same circle.

 Inside the circle

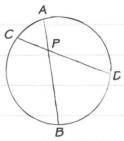

$$AP \times PB = CP \times PD$$

 Outside the circle

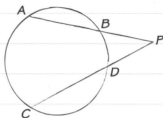

$$AP \times PB = CP \times PD$$

These two rules are the same — note that all four line segments used in the formula end at the point of intersection, P. These rules are not on the formula sheet, so LEARN them.

 Worked example

Aiming higher

PTR and QTS are chords of a circle.

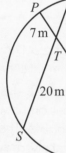

$PT = 7\,\text{m}$
$ST = 20\,\text{m}$
$RT = 32\,\text{m}$
$QT = x\,\text{cm}$

Calculate the value of x. **(2 marks)**

$ST \times QT = PT \times RT$

$20 \times x = 7 \times 32$

$20x = 224 \quad (\div 20)$

$x = 11.2$

Write down the formula before you substitute any values. Then substitute the values you are given and solve the equation to find x.

Check it!
Make sure you are multiplying line segments on the **same** line:

ST and QT ✓　　　　PT and RT ✓

Chord and tangent

If a chord intersects with a tangent, then you can use this special case:

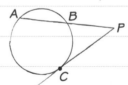

$$AP \times BP = CP^2$$

 Now try this

Aiming higher

AB and CD are chords of a circle.
EP is a tangent to the circle.
$AB = 2$ cm, $BP = 3$ cm and $DP = 2.5$ cm
$CD = x$ cm and $EP = y$ cm

(a) Calculate the value of x. **(3 marks)**

(b) Calculate the value of y, giving your answer correct to 1 decimal place. **(2 marks)**

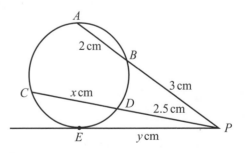

Be really careful with part (a). You will be using the formula $AP \times BP = CP \times DP$ so you need to use the following lengths:

$AP = 2 + 3 = 5$ cm　　　　$BP = 3$ cm　　　$DP = 2.5$ cm

The formula will tell you the length of CP, so you need to subtract 2.5 to find x.

Perimeter and area

Triangle

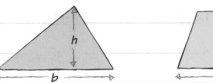

Area = $\frac{1}{2}bh$
Learn this formula ✓

Parallelogram

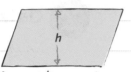

Area = bh
Learn this formula ✓

Trapezium

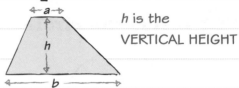

h is the
VERTICAL HEIGHT

Area = $\frac{1}{2}(a + b)h$
Given on the formula sheet ✓

You can calculate areas and perimeters of more complex shapes by splitting them into parts.

You might need to draw some extra lines on your diagram and add or subtract areas.

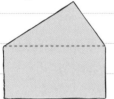

Area = rectangle + triangle

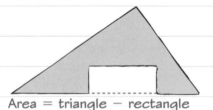

Area = triangle − rectangle

Area basics

Lengths are all in the same units.

Give units with the answer.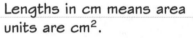

Lengths in cm means area units are cm².

Lengths in m means area units are m².

Worked example

The diagram shows a garden.

Adrian wants to cover the garden with grass seed.

A packet of grass seed will cover 10 m².

4.5 m
3 m   Not drawn accurately
6 m
4 m
3 m
8.5 m

(a) How many packets of grass seed does Adrian need to buy? **(3 marks)**

Area = 6 × 4.5 + 4 × 3 = 27 + 12 = 39 m²

Adrian needs to buy 4 packets of grass seed.

Adrian also wants to build a fence around the edge of the garden.

(b) Calculate the total length of Adrian's fence. **(1 mark)**

6 + 4.5 + 3 + 4 + 3 + 8.5 = 29 m

Draw a dotted line to divide the diagram into two rectangles.

You have to use the information in the question to work out the missing lengths. The diagram is **not accurately drawn**, so you can't use a ruler to measure.

8.5 m − 4.5 m = 4 m

6 m − 3 m = 3 m

Write these lengths on your diagram.

Make sure you answer the question that has been asked.

You need to say how many packets of grass seed Adrian needs to buy.

Now try this

Work out the area of this shape. **(4 marks)**

Divide the shape into a rectangle and a triangle, then calculate any unknown lengths by subtracting.

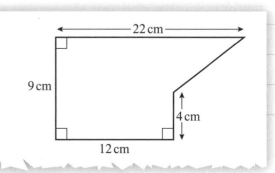

22 cm
9 cm
4 cm
12 cm

Prisms

A prism is a 3-D shape with a constant CROSS-SECTION. If the cross-section is a rectangle then we call the prism a cuboid.

Cuboid

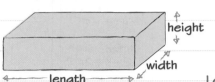

Volume = length × width × height   Learn this formula ✓

Prism

Cross-section   length

Given on the formula sheet ✓

Volume = area of cross-section × length

You might need to work out the area of the cross-section before working out the volume of the prism.

You should draw a sketch of the cross-section separately to work out its area.

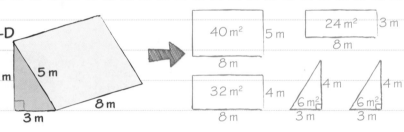

Area of cross-section = area of rectangle + area of triangle

$$= 7 \times 4 + \frac{1}{2} \times 7 \times 2 = 35 \text{ cm}^2$$

Volume of prism = 35 × 10 = 350 cm³

Surface area

To work out the surface area of a 3-D shape, you need to add together the areas of all the faces.

It's a good idea to sketch each face with its dimensions.

Remember to include the faces that you can't see.

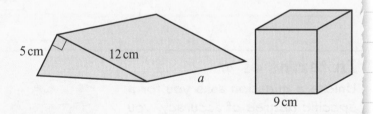

Surface area = 40 + 32 + 24 + 6 + 6 = 108 m²

Worked example

The diagram shows a triangular prism and a cube. They both have the **same** volume.

Work out the length of *a*.   **(4 marks)**

Volume of cube = 9^3 = 729 cm³

Volume of prism = Area of cross-
          section × length

          $= \frac{1}{2} \times 5 \times 12 \times a$

          $= 30a$

30a = 729

a = 24.3 cm

5 cm   12 cm   a   9 cm

Calculate the volume of the cube, and write an expression for the volume of the prism. Set these equal to each other and solve the equation to find *a*.

Now try this

The diagram shows a 3-D shape with a cross-section made from a rectangle and a triangle.

Calculate the volume of the shape.

State the units of your answer.   **(4 marks)**

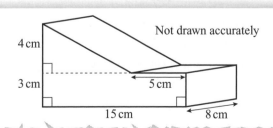

Not drawn accurately

4 cm

3 cm   5 cm

15 cm   8 cm

Circles and cylinders

You need to learn these formulae for circles and cylinders. They're not on the formula sheet.

Circle

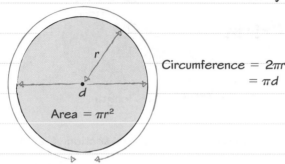

Circumference $= 2\pi r$
$= \pi d$

Area $= \pi r^2$

Cylinder

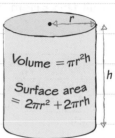

Volume $= \pi r^2 h$

Surface area $= 2\pi r^2 + 2\pi rh$

Worked example

The diagram shows a game counter in the shape of a semicircle.

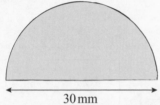

30 mm

Work out the area of the counter. Give your answer correct to 2 significant figures. **(3 marks)**

Radius $= 30 \div 2 = 15$ mm

Area of circle $= \pi r^2$

$\qquad = \pi \times 15^2$

$\qquad = 706.8583...$ mm^2

Area of counter $= 706.8583... \div 2$

$\qquad = 350$ mm^2 (2 s.f.)

Calculator skills

Make sure you know how to enter π on your calculator. On some calculators you have to press these keys:

SHIFT $\quad\quad \pi \quad e$

$\boxed{\times 10^{\text{x}}} \quad \blacktriangleright \quad \boxed{\times 10^{\text{x}}}$

EXAM ALERT!

The formula for the area of a circle uses the **radius**. If the length shown on the diagram is the **diameter**, you need to divide it by 2 before you substitute into the formula. Don't round any values until the end of your working.

Students have struggled with exam questions similar to this – **be prepared!**

In terms of π

Unless a question asks you for a specific degree of accuracy, you can give your answers as a whole number or fraction multiplied by π. An answer given in terms of π is an EXACT ANSWER rather than a ROUNDED ANSWER.

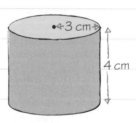

4 cm

Volume of cylinder $= \pi r^2 h$

$\qquad\qquad\qquad = \pi \times 3^2 \times 4$

EXACT ANSWER

Volume $= 36\pi$ cm^3

ROUNDED ANSWER

Volume $= 113$ cm^3 (to 3 s.f.)

Now try this

This shape is made from a rectangle and a semicircle.

Work out the area of the shape.

Give your answer correct to 3 significant figures. **(4 marks)**

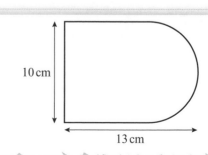

10 cm

13 cm

Volumes of 3-D shapes

Cylinder

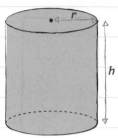

Volume of cylinder
= area of base × height
= $\pi r^2 h$

Pyramid

Volume of pyramid
= $\frac{1}{3}$ × area of base
    × vertical height
= $\frac{1}{3}Ah$

Learn these volume formulae ✓

Cone

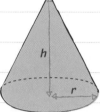

Volume of cone
= $\frac{1}{3}$ × area of base × vertical height
= $\frac{1}{3}\pi r^2 h$

Sphere

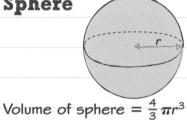

Volume of sphere = $\frac{4}{3}\pi r^3$

These volume formulae are on the formula sheet ✓

Copy the formula from the formulae sheet before you substitute. You can give your answer in terms of π or to 3 s.f.

Worked example   Aiming higher

The diagram shows a solid cone.

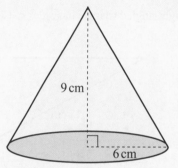

Work out the volume of the cone. **(2 marks)**

Volume = $\frac{1}{3}\pi r^2 h$
= $\frac{1}{3} \times \pi \times 6^2 \times 9$
= 108π cm³
= 339 cm³ (3 s.f.)

Now try this

1 These two cylinders have the same volume.   Aiming higher

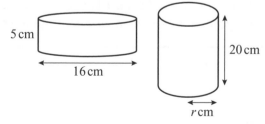

Work out the radius, r of the second cylinder. **(4 marks)**

Give your fraction in the lowest terms possible.

2 A tennis ball of diameter 7 cm is packaged in a cylindrical box. The ball touches the sides, top and base of the box.

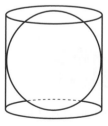

Work out the fraction of the volume of the box taken up by the tennis ball. You must show your working. **(3 marks)**

Pythagoras' theorem

Pythagoras' theorem is a really useful rule. You can use it to find the length of a missing side in a right-angled triangle.

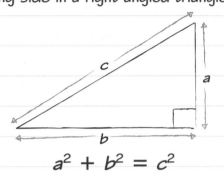

$$a^2 + b^2 = c^2$$

Pythagoras checklist

$short^2 + short^2 = long^2$ ✓

Right-angled triangle. ✓

Lengths of two sides known. ✓

Length of third side missing. ✓

Learn this. It's not on the formula sheet. ✓

Worked example

This right-angled triangle has sides x, 17 cm and 8 cm.

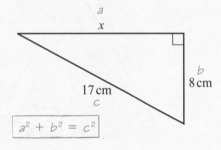

$a^2 + b^2 = c^2$

Show that $x = 15$ cm **(3 marks)**

$$x^2 + 8^2 = 17^2$$
$$x^2 = 17^2 - 8^2$$
$$= 225$$
$$x = \sqrt{225} = 15 \text{ cm}$$

The question says "Show that" so you have to show **all** your working. Be careful when the missing length is one of the **shorter** sides.

1. Label the longest side of the triangle c.
2. Label the other two sides a and b.
3. Write out the formula for Pythagoras' theorem.
4. Substitute the values for a, b and c into the formula.
5. Rearrange the formula and solve. Make sure you show **every step** in your working.
6. Write units in your answer.

Pythagoras questions come in lots of different forms. Just look for the right-angled triangle.

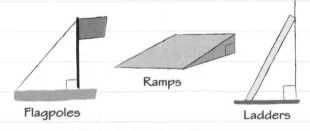

Ramps

Flagpoles

Ladders

Calculator skills

Use these buttons to find squares and square roots with your calculator.

You might need to use the S⇔D key to get your answer as a decimal number.

Now try this

(a) Work out the value of y. **(3 marks)**

(b) Use your value of y to work out the value of z. **(3 marks)**

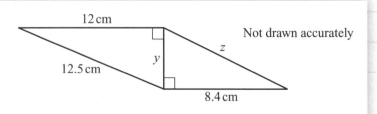

Not drawn accurately

Pythagoras in 3-D

To tackle the most demanding questions, you need to be able to use Pythagoras' theorem in 3-D shapes.

You can use Pythagoras' theorem to find the length of the longest diagonal in a cuboid.

You can also use Pythagoras to find missing lengths in pyramids and cones.

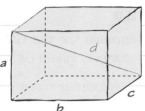

$$a^2 + b^2 + c^2 = d^2$$

Why does it work?

You can use 2-D Pythagoras twice to show why the formula for 3-D Pythagoras works.

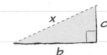

$$x^2 = b^2 + c^2$$

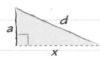

$$d^2 = a^2 + x^2$$
$$= a^2 + b^2 + c^2$$

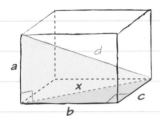
Worked example

Aiming higher

The diagram shows a cuboid. Work out the length of PQ.
(3 marks)

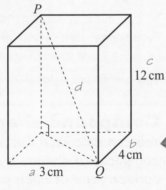

$$d^2 = a^2 + b^2 + c^2$$
$$PQ^2 = 3^2 + 4^2 + 12^2$$
$$= 169$$
$$PQ = \sqrt{169} = 13$$
So PQ is 13 cm.

Write out the formula for Pythagoras in 3-D. Label the sides of the cuboid a, b and c, and label the long diagonal d.

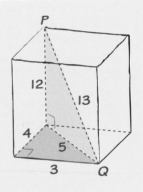

You could also answer this question by sketching two right-angled triangles and using 2-D Pythagoras.

Check it!

The diagonal must be longer than any of the other three lengths.

13 cm looks about right. ✓

Now try this

Aiming higher

This is a diagram of a wedge.

Angles TXW, TXY and XYW are all 90°.

(a) Work out the length of TW.
Give your answer to 1 decimal place. **(3 marks)**

(b) **Without further calculation**, give reasons as to which of angles TWX or TYX is larger. **(2 marks)**

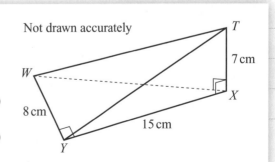

Not drawn accurately

Surface area

Cone

The formula for the CURVED SURFACE AREA of a cone is given on the formula sheet.

> **Curved surface area of cone = $\pi r \ell$**
>
>
>
> Be careful! This formula uses the slant height, ℓ, of the cone.

To calculate the TOTAL surface area of the cone you need to add the area of the base. Surface area of cone = $\pi r^2 + \pi r \ell$

Sphere

The formula for the surface area of a sphere is given on the formula sheet.

> **Surface area of sphere = $4\pi r^2$**
>
>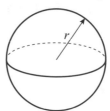
>
> For a reminder about areas of circles and surface areas of cylinders have a look at page 64.

A hemisphere is half a sphere, so the area of the curved surface is $\frac{1}{2} \times 4\pi r^2$

Worked example

Aiming higher

The diagram shows a cone with vertical height 12 cm and base diameter 10 cm.

Work out the curved surface area of the cone.

(4 marks)

$r = 5$

$\ell^2 = 12^2 + 5^2 = 169$

$\ell = 13$ cm

Curved surface area
$= \pi r \ell$
$= \pi \times 13 \times 5$
$= 65\pi$ cm^2

To work out the curved surface area you need to know the radius and the slant height. You are given the **diameter** and the **vertical height**.

The radius is half the diameter = 5 cm.

To calculate the slant height you need to use Pythagoras' theorem. Sketch the right-angled triangle containing the missing length.

You can leave your answer in terms of π.

Compound shapes

You can calculate the surface area of more complicated shapes by adding together the surface area of each part.

Surface area $= \pi(4)^2 + 2\pi(4)(6) + \frac{1}{2}[4\pi(4)^2]$
$= 96\pi$ cm^2

Now try this

Aiming higher

A cone has a base diameter of 16 cm and a vertical height of 15 cm.

The cone is cut in half vertically through the vertex.

The diagram shows one of the half-cones.

Work out the total surface area of the half-cone.

Give your answer correct to 3 significant figures.

(5 marks)

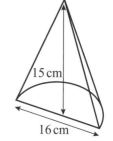

Speed

This is the formula triangle for speed.

Average speed •——
——• Distance
——• Time

Average speed = $\dfrac{\text{total distance travelled}}{\text{total time taken}}$

Time = $\dfrac{\text{distance}}{\text{average speed}}$

Distance = average speed × time

Using a formula triangle

Cover up the quantity you want to find with your finger.

The position of the other two quantities tells you the formula.

$T = \dfrac{D}{S}$ $S = \dfrac{D}{T}$ $D = S \times T$

Units

The most common units of speed are:

• metres per second: m/s

• kilometres per hour: km/h

• miles per hour: mph.

The units in your answer will depend on the units you use in the formula.

When distance is measured in km and time is measured in hours, speed will be measured in km/h.

When you are calculating a distance or time, you MUST make sure that the units of the other quantities match.

Minutes and hours

For questions on speed, you need to be able to convert between minutes and hours.

Remember there are 60 minutes in 1 hour.

To convert from minutes to hours you divide by 60.

24 minutes = 0.4 hours $\dfrac{24}{60} = \dfrac{2}{5} = 0.4$

To convert from hours to minutes you multiply by 60.

3.2 hours = 192 minutes $3.2 \times 60 = 192$
= 3 hours 12 minutes

A plane travels at a constant speed of 600 km/h for 45 minutes.

How far has it travelled?   **(2 marks)**

45 minutes = $\dfrac{45}{60}$ hours = $\dfrac{3}{4}$ hour

D = S × T
= $600 \times \dfrac{3}{4} = \dfrac{600 \times 3}{4} = \dfrac{1800}{4} = 450$

The plane has travelled 450 km.

Speed checklist

Draw formula triangle.

Make sure units match.

Give units with answer.

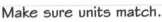

Draw the formula triangle on your exam paper. You need to make sure the units match so start by converting 45 minutes into hours.

1 Bradley cycled 172 km at an average speed of 40 kilometres per hour.

   How long did it take him?

   Give your answer in hours and minutes.   **(3 marks)**

2 Nisha drives from Newcastle to Oxford.

   Her average speed is 55 mph.

   The journey takes 4 hours 48 minutes

   How far did she drive?   **(3 marks)**

Converting units

You can convert between METRIC UNITS by multiplying or dividing by 10, 100 or 1000.

Length

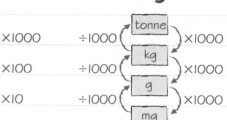

Weight

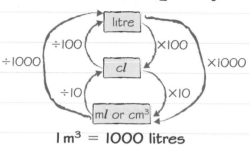

Volume or capacity

$1 m^3 = 1000$ litres

Units of area and volume

In your exam, you may be asked to convert between different units of area and volume.
These two squares have the same area.

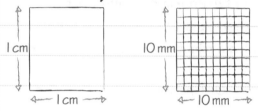

So $1 cm^2 = 100 mm^2$

These two cubes have the same volume.

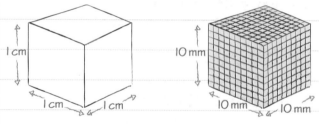

So $1 cm^3 = 1000 mm^3$

Area conversions

$1 cm^2 = 10^2 mm^2 = 100 mm^2$

$1 m^2 = 100^2 cm^2 = 10\,000 cm^2$

$1 km^2 = 1000^2 m^2 = 1\,000\,000 m^2$

Volume conversions

$1 cm^3 = 10^3 mm^3 = 1000 mm^3$

$1 m^3 = 100^3 cm^3 = 1\,000\,000 cm^3$

1 litre $= 1000 cm^3$

$1 m\ell = 1 cm^3$

Converting compound units

To convert between measures of speed you need to convert one unit first then the other. Write the new units at each step of your working. To convert 72 km/h into m/s:

72 km/h $\rightarrow 72 \times 1000 = 72\,000$ m/h

$72\,000$ m/h $\rightarrow 72\,000 \div 3600 = 20$ m/s

1 hour $= 60 \times 60 = 3600$ seconds

Worked example

Change 275 cm^3 into mm^3.   **(1 mark)**

$275 \times 10^3 = 275\,000$

$275 cm^3 = 275\,000 mm^3$

To convert from cm to mm you multiply by 10, so to convert from cm^3 to mm^3 you multiply by 10^3.

Now try this

1 A cheetah can run at speeds of up to 31 metres per second.

Convert 31 m/s into km/h.   **(2 marks)**

2 Change
(a) 1.8 m^2 to cm^2 **(1 mark)**
(b) 4250 mm^2 to cm^2 **(1 mark)**
(c) 840 000 cm^3 to m^3 **(1 mark)**

Similar shapes 1

Shapes are SIMILAR if one shape is an enlargement of the other.

SIMILAR TRIANGLES satisfy these three conditions:

 1 All three pairs of angles are equal.

 2 All three pairs of sides are in the same ratio.

 3 Two sides are in the same ratio and the included angle is equal.

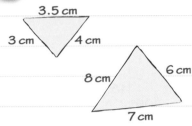
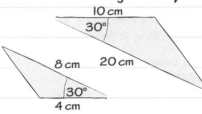

Worked example

XYZ and ABC are similar triangles.

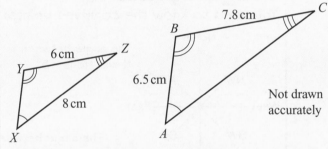

Not drawn accurately

(a) Work out the length of AC. **(2 marks)**

$$\frac{AC}{XZ} = \frac{BC}{YZ}$$

$$\frac{AC}{8} = \frac{7.8}{6}$$

$$AC = \frac{7.8 \times 8}{6}$$

$$= 10.4 \text{ cm}$$

(b) Work out the length of XY. **(2 marks)**

$$\frac{XY}{AB} = \frac{YZ}{BC}$$

$$\frac{XY}{6.5} = \frac{6}{7.8}$$

$$XY = \frac{6 \times 6.5}{7.8}$$

$$= 5 \text{ cm}$$

> Start with the unknown length on top of a fraction. Make sure you write your ratios in the correct order.

Similar shapes checklist

Use these facts to solve similar shapes problems:

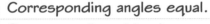 Corresponding angles equal. ✓

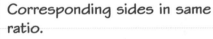 Corresponding sides in same ratio. ✓

Spotting similar triangles

Here are some similar triangles:

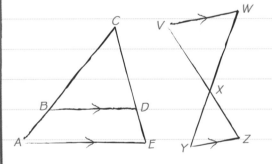

Triangle ACE is similar to triangle BCD

Triangle VWX is similar to triangle ZYX

Now try this

Triangles ABC and PQR are similar.

Angle ACB = angle PRQ

(a) Work out the size of angle PRQ. **(2 marks)**

(b) Work out the length of PQ. **(2 marks)**

Not drawn accurately

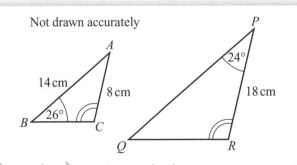

Bearings

Bearings are measured CLOCKWISE from NORTH.

Bearings always have THREE FIGURES, so you need to add zeros if the angle is less than 100°. For instance, in this diagram the bearing of B from A is 048°.

You can measure a bearing bigger than 180° by measuring this angle and subtracting it from 360°.

The bearing of C from A is 360° − 109° = 251°

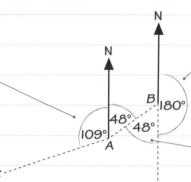

You can work out a reverse bearing by adding or subtracting 180°.

The bearing of A from B is 180° + 048° = 228°

These are alternate angles.

Worked example

Three paths meet at *O. B* is due East of *O*.

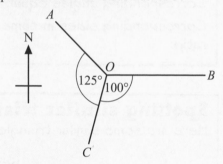

(a) Jake walks from *O* to *A*.
     What bearing does he walk on?   **(2 marks)**

90° + 100° + 125° = 315°

(b) Delvinder walks from *C* to *O*.
     What bearing does she walk on?   **(2 marks)**

Bearing of C from O = 90° + 100°

= 190°

Bearing of O from C = 190° − 180° = 010°

Compass points

You need to know the compass points:

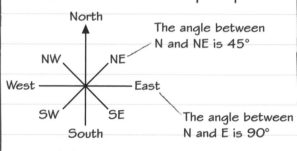

The angle between N and NE is 45°

The angle between N and E is 90°

EXAM ALERT!

You can work out a **reverse** bearing by adding or subtracting 180°. If the angle is greater than 180° then subtract. Remember to write your final answer as a **three-figure bearing**. You need to write 010° not just 10°.

Students have struggled with exam questions similar to this – **be prepared!**

Now try this

An aircraft flies from *A* to *B*.

(a) Measure and write down the bearing of *B* from *A*.   **(1 mark)**

The aircraft then flies to a point *C*. The bearing of *C* from *B* is 080° and the bearing of *C* from *A* is 120°.

(b) Mark the position of *C* on the diagram.   **(3 marks)**

Remember bearings have **three figures** and are measured **clockwise** from **North**.

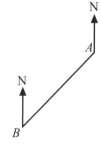

Scale drawings and maps

This is a SCALE DRAWING of the Queen Mary II cruise ship.

Scale = 1 : 50 000

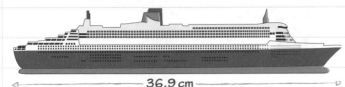

|← 36.9 cm →|

You can use the scale to work out the length of the actual ship.

36.9 × 50 000 = 34 500

The ship is 34 500 cm or 345 m long.

Map scales

Map scales can be written in different ways:

MAP
SCALE
1 : 25 000

* 1 to 25 000
* 1 cm represents 25 000 cm
* 1 cm represents 250 m
* 4 cm represent 1 km

The diagram shows a scale drawing of a port and a lighthouse.

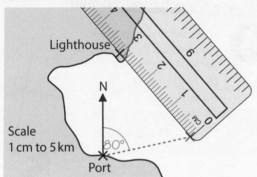

Lighthouse

N

Scale
1 cm to 5 km

80°

Port

A boat sails 12 km in a straight line on a bearing of 080°.

(a) Mark the new position of the boat with a cross. **(2 marks)**

(b) How far away is the boat from the lighthouse? Give your answer in km. **(1 mark)**

15 km

For a reminder about bearings have a look at page 72.

Start by working out how far the boat is from the port on the scale drawing.

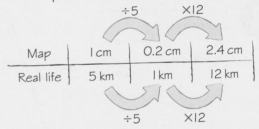

	÷5		×12
Map	1 cm	0.2 cm	2.4 cm
Real life	5 km	1 km	12 km
	÷5		×12

Now place the centre of your protractor on the port with the zero line pointing North. Put a dot at 80°. Line up your ruler between the port and the dot. Draw a cross 2.4 cm from the port.

Use a ruler to measure the distance from the lighthouse to the boat. 3 cm on the drawing represents 15 km in real life.

---

1 A map uses a scale of 1 : 150 000

Two towns are 6 cm apart on the map.

How far apart are they in real life?

Give your answer in kilometres. **(3 marks)**

2 On a map, a distance of 8 cm represents a real-life distance of 1 km.

Write the scale of the map in the form 1 : *n* **(2 marks)**

Constructions

"Construct" means "draw accurately using a ruler and compasses". For your exam you should make sure you have a good pair of compasses with stiff arms and a sharp pencil.

Worked example

1 Use ruler and compasses to **construct** a triangle with sides of length 3 cm, 4 cm and 5.5 cm.

(2 marks)

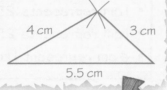

Draw and label one side with a ruler. Then use your compasses to find the other vertex.

Worked example

2 Use ruler and compasses to **construct** the bisector of angle *PQR*.   **(2 marks)**

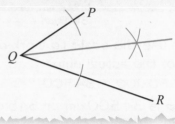

Mark points on each arm an equal distance from Q. Then use arcs to find a third point an equal distance from these two points.

Worked example

3 Use ruler and compasses to **construct** the perpendicular bisector of the line *AB*.

(2 marks)

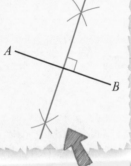

Use your compasses to draw intersecting arcs with centres at A and B. Remember to show **all** your construction lines and arcs.

Worked example

4 Use ruler and compasses to **construct** the perpendicular to the line segment *AB* that passes through point *P*.

(2 marks)

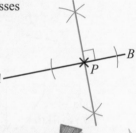

Use your compasses to mark two points on the line an equal distance from P. Then widen your compasses and draw arcs with their centres at these two points.

Now try this

1 Use ruler and compasses to construct the perpendicular bisector of the line *AB*.

Show all your construction lines.   **(2 marks)**

2 Use ruler and compasses to construct an angle of 60° at *X*. Show all your construction lines.

(2 marks)

X ——————————— Y

Construct an equilateral triangle.

Translations, reflections and rotations

You might have to describe these transformations in your exam. To describe a translation you need to give a vector. To describe a reflection you need to give the equation of the mirror line. To describe a rotation you need to give the direction, the angle and the centre of rotation.

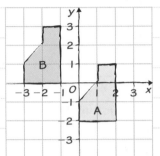

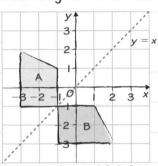

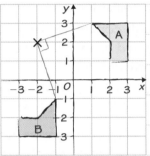

A to B: TRANSLATION by the vector $\begin{pmatrix} -3 \\ 2 \end{pmatrix}$

A to B: REFLECTION in the line $y = x$

A to B: ROTATION 90° clockwise about the point (−2, 2)

You can ask for tracing paper in an exam. This makes it easy to rotate shapes and check your answers.

For all three transformations, shape B is CONGRUENT to shape A. This means that they are exactly the same shape and size. Lengths of sides and angles do not change.

Worked example

The diagram shows two shapes **P** and **Q**.

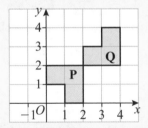

Describe fully the single transformation which takes shape **P** to shape **Q**.   **(3 marks)**

Rotation 90° clockwise with centre (3, 1).

EXAM ALERT!

To **fully describe** a rotation you need to write down:
- the word 'rotation'
- the angle of turn and the direction
- the centre of rotation.

Be careful when the shapes are joined at one corner. This point is not necessarily the centre of rotation.

Check it!
You are allowed to ask for tracing paper in your exam. Trace shape **P** and put your pencil on your centre of rotation. Rotate the tracing paper to see if the shapes match up. ✓

Students have struggled with exam questions similar to this – **be prepared!**

Now try this

Triangles **A**, **B** and **C** are shown on the grid.

(a) Describe fully the **single** transformation that takes triangle **A** onto triangle **B**.   **(3 marks)**

(b) Describe fully the translation that takes triangle **A** onto triangle **C**.   **(1 mark)**

This is a **translation**. Either write the **vector**, or write "☐ units in the x-direction and ☐ units in the y-direction."

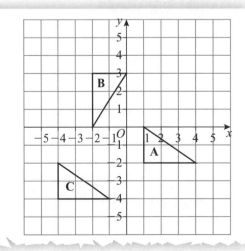

Enlargements

To describe an enlargement you need to give the scale factor and the centre of enlargement.

The SCALE FACTOR of an enlargement tells you how much each length is multiplied by.

$$\text{Scale factor} = \frac{\text{enlarged length}}{\text{original length}}$$

Lines drawn through corresponding points on the object (A) and image (B) meet at the CENTRE OF ENLARGEMENT.

When the scale factor is between 0 and 1, image B is SMALLER than object A.

For enlargements, angles in shapes do not change but lengths of sides do change.

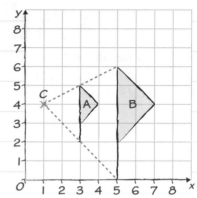

A to B: Each point on B is twice as far from C as the corresponding point on A.

Enlargement with scale factor 2, centre (1, 4)

Worked example

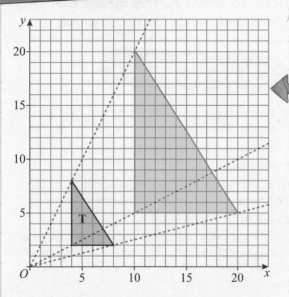

On the grid, enlarge triangle **T** with a scale factor of $2\frac{1}{2}$ and centre (0, 0)   **(3 marks)**

1. Draw lines from the centre of enlargement through each vertex of the triangle.

2. For each vertex, multiply the vertical and horizontal distances from the centre of enlargement by $2\frac{1}{2}$

   For the top vertex:

   Horizontal distance $= 4 \times 2\frac{1}{2} = 10$

   Vertical distance $= 8 \times 2\frac{1}{2} = 20$

   The corresponding vertex on the image is 10 squares horizontally and 20 squares vertically from the centre of enlargement.

3. Join up your vertices with straight lines.

Check it!

Each length on the image should be $2\frac{1}{2}$ times the corresponding length on the object. The image is **mathematically similar** to the object, so check it looks the same shape.

There is more on similar shapes on pages 71 and 85.

Now try this

Triangle **A** is shown on the grid.

(a) Enlarge triangle **A** with a scale factor of 2 and centre of enlargement (6, 5)
Label the image **B**.   **(2 marks)**

(b) Enlarge triangle **A** with a scale factor of $\frac{1}{2}$ and centre of enlargement (−7, 3)
Label the image **C**.   **(3 marks)**

The scale factor is a **fraction** so the image will be **smaller** than the object.

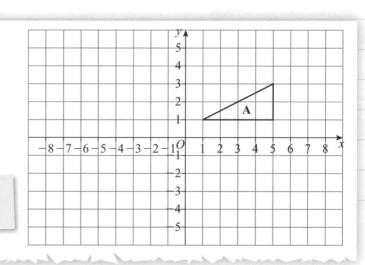

Combining transformations

You can describe two or more transformations using a single transformation.

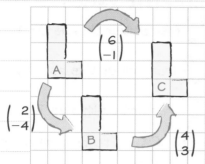

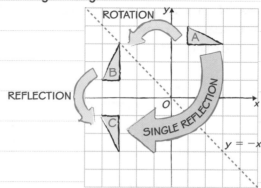

A to B to C: A translation $\begin{pmatrix}2\\-4\end{pmatrix}$ followed by a translation $\begin{pmatrix}4\\3\end{pmatrix}$ is the same as a single translation $\begin{pmatrix}6\\-1\end{pmatrix}$

A to B to C: A rotation 90° anticlockwise about O followed by a reflection in the x-axis is the same as a single reflection in the line $y = -x$

Worked example

Triangle **A** is shown on the grid.

(a) Reflect triangle **A** in the y-axis. Label your new triangle **B**. **(1 mark)**

(b) Triangle **B** is reflected in the line $y = 1$ to give triangle **C**. Describe fully the **single** transformation which takes triangle **A** onto triangle **C**. **(4 marks)**

Rotation 180° about the point (0, 1)

To answer part (b) you need to draw
• the line $y = 1$
• the new triangle, **C**.

For a rotation of 180° you don't need to give a direction.

Check it!
You can ask for tracing paper in the exam.
Check a reflection by folding the tracing paper along the symmetry line. ✓

Describe fully...
A translation: vector of translation. ✓
A reflection: equation of mirror line. ✓
A rotation: angle of turn, direction of turn and centre of rotation. ✓
An enlargement: scale factor and centre of enlargement. ✓

Now try this

Triangle **A** is shown on the grid.

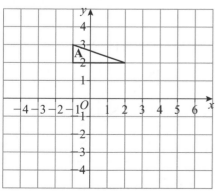

(a) Translate triangle **A** by the vector $\begin{pmatrix}3\\-3\end{pmatrix}$ Label the image **B**. **(2 marks)**

(b) Rotate triangle **B** 90° clockwise about (0, 1) Label the image **C**. **(2 marks)**

(c) Describe fully the **single** transformation that takes triangle **C** onto triangle **A**. **(3 marks)**

Check a rotation by putting your pencil on the centre of rotation and turning the tracing paper. ✓

Trigonometry 1

You can use the trigonometric ratios to find the size of an angle in a right-angled triangle. You need to know the lengths of two sides of the triangle.

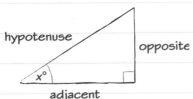

The sides of the triangle are labelled relative to the ANGLE you need to find.

Trigonometric ratios

$\sin x° = \dfrac{\text{opp}}{\text{hyp}}$ (remember this as S^O_H)

$\cos x° = \dfrac{\text{adj}}{\text{hyp}}$ (remember this as C^A_H)

$\tan x° = \dfrac{\text{opp}}{\text{adj}}$ (remember this as T^O_A)

You can use $S^O_H C^A_H T^O_A$ to remember these rules for trig ratios.

These rules only work for RIGHT-ANGLED triangles.

Worked example

Calculate the size of angle x.   **(3 marks)**

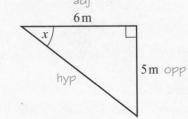

$\tan x° = \dfrac{\text{opp}}{\text{adj}} = \dfrac{5}{6}$

$x° = 39.805\,571\,09° = 39.8°$ (to 3 s.f.)

Label the **hyp**otenuse first — it's the longest side.

Then label the side **adj**acent to the angle you want to work out.

Finally label the side **opp**osite the angle you want to work out.

Remember $S^O_H C^A_H T^O_A$. You know **opp** and **adj** here so use T^O_A.

Do **not** "divide by tan" to get x on its own. You need to use the $\tan^{-1}$ function on your calculator.

$$\tan^{-1}\left(\dfrac{5}{6}\right)$$
39.80557109

Write down all the figures on your calculator display then round your answer.

Using your calculator

To find a missing angle using trigonometry you have to use one of these functions.

$$\sin^{-1} \qquad \cos^{-1} \qquad \tan^{-1}$$

These are called INVERSE TRIGONOMETRIC functions. They are the inverse operations of sin, cos and tan.

Make sure that your calculator is in degree mode. Look for the **D** symbol at the top of the display.

Now try this

Work out the size of angle x in each of these triangles. Give your answers correct to 1 decimal place.

(a)

4.3 cm   6.1 cm

x

(3 marks)

(b)

11.2 cm

x
7.5 cm

(3 marks)

(c)

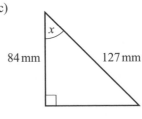

x

84 mm   127 mm

(3 marks)

Trigonometry 2

You can use the trigonometric ratios to find the length of a missing side in a right-angled triangle. You need to know the length of another side and the size of one of the acute angles.

Worked example

Calculate the length of side a. **(3 marks)**

$$\sin x° = \frac{opp}{hyp}$$

$$\sin 40° = \frac{a}{10}$$

$$a = 10 \times \sin 40°$$

$$= 6.42787...$$

$$= 6.43\,cm \text{ (to 3 s.f.)}$$

Write down at least four figures of the calculator display before giving your final answer correct to 3 significant figures.

Check it!

Side a must be shorter than the hypotenuse. 6.43 cm looks about right. ✓

Label the sides of the triangle relative to the 40° angle. Write $S^O_H C^A_H T^O_A$ and tick the pieces of information you have. You need to use S^O_H here.

Write the values you know in the rule and replace **opp** with a. You can solve this equation to find the value of a.

Angles of elevation and depression

Some trigonometry questions will involve angles of elevation and depression.

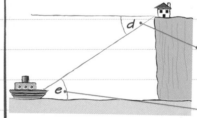

The angle of depression of the ship from the house.

The angle of elevation of the house from the ship.

Angles of elevation and depression are always measured from the horizontal.

In this diagram, $d = e$ because they are alternate angles.

Now try this

Work out the length of side a in each of these triangles.
Give your answers correct to 1 decimal place.

In part (c) a is the hypotenuse. It will be on the bottom of the fraction when you substitute, so be careful with your calculation.

(a)
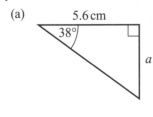

(3 marks)

(b)
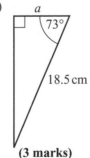

(3 marks)

(c)
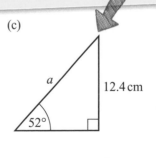

(3 marks)

The sine rule

The SINE RULE applies to any triangle. You don't need a right angle.

You label the angles of the triangle with capital letters and the sides with lower case letters. Each side has the same letter as its OPPOSITE angle.

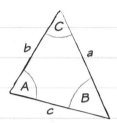

$$\frac{a}{\sin A} = \frac{b}{\sin B} = \frac{c}{\sin C}$$

This version is given on the formula sheet. Use it to find a missing side.

$$\frac{\sin A}{a} = \frac{\sin B}{b} = \frac{\sin C}{c}$$

Learn this version. It's useful for finding a missing angle.

Worked example

Aiming higher

Calculate the size of angle x.   **(3 marks)**

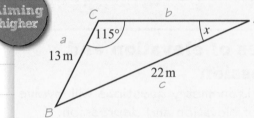

$$\frac{\sin A}{a} = \frac{\sin C}{c}$$

$$\frac{\sin x}{13} = \frac{\sin 115°}{22}$$

$$\sin x = \frac{13 \times \sin 115°}{22}$$

$$= 0.5355...$$

$$x = 32.4° \text{ (3 s.f.)}$$

Golden rule

To use the sine rule you need to know a side length and the OPPOSITE angle.

EXAM ALERT!

This is not a right-angled triangle so you can't use $S^O_H\, C^A_H\, T^O_A$. To find an angle use the 'upside down' version of the sine rule. You're not interested in side b or angle B so ignore this part of the rule.

Start by writing the value you want to find on top of the first fraction. Then substitute the other values you know and solve an equation to find x. Use the $\sin^{-1}$ function on your calculator.

Students have struggled with exam questions similar to this – **be prepared!**

Worked example

Aiming higher

Calculate the length of AC.   **(3 marks)**

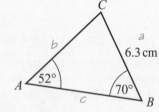

$$\frac{b}{\sin B} = \frac{a}{\sin A}$$

$$\frac{AC}{\sin 70°} = \frac{6.3}{\sin 52°}$$

$$AC = \frac{6.3 \times \sin 70°}{\sin 52°}$$

$$= 7.5126...$$

$$= 7.5 \text{ cm (2 s.f.)}$$

You know a side length and the opposite angle so you can use the sine rule.

Check it!
The greater side length is opposite the greater angle. ✓

Now try this

Aiming higher

In triangle ABC, $AB = 11$ cm, $AC = 13$ cm and angle $ABC = 57°$

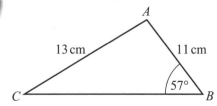

(a) Work out the size of angle ACB.   **(3 marks)**

(b) Work out the length of BC.   **(3 marks)**

The cosine rule

The COSINE RULE applies to any triangle. You don't need a right angle.

You usually use the cosine rule when you are given two sides and the included angle (SAS) or when you are given three sides and want to work out an angle (SSS).

$$a^2 = b^2 + c^2 - 2bc \cos A$$

This version is on the formula sheet. Use it to find a missing side.

$$\cos A = \frac{b^2 + c^2 - a^2}{2bc}$$

Learn this version. It's useful for finding a missing angle.

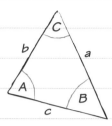

Which rule?

This chart shows you which rule to use when solving trigonometry problems in triangles:

Right-angled triangle? → NO → Side and the opposite angle given? → NO → Use the cosine rule

Right-angled triangle? ↓ YES → Use $S^O_H C^A_H T^O_A$

Side and the opposite angle given? ↓ YES → Use the sine rule

Worked example

Aiming higher

PQRS is a trapezium. Work out the length of the diagonal *PR*. **(3 marks)**

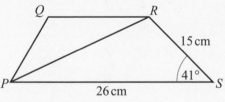

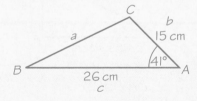

$$a^2 = b^2 + c^2 - 2bc \cos A$$
$$PR^2 = 15^2 + 26^2 - 2 \times 15 \times 26 \times \cos 41°$$
$$= 312.3265...$$
$$PR = 17.6727... = 17.7 \text{ cm (3 s.f.)}$$

If you are given a more complicated diagram it is sometimes useful to sketch a triangle. Label your triangle with *a* as the missing side.

This is not a right-angled triangle so you can't use $S^O_H C^A_H T^O_A$. You know two sides and the included angle (SAS) so you can use the cosine rule.

Substitute the values you know into the formula. Work out the right-hand side using your calculator, but don't round your answer yet.

Use √☐ Ans on your calculator to find the final answer.

Round to 3 significant figures or to the same degree of accuracy as the original measurements. Because this answer shows all its workings, you could give either 17.7 cm or 18 cm as the answer.

Now try this

Aiming higher

Triangle *PQR* has sides of 9 cm, 10 cm and 14 cm.

P, 10 cm, 9 cm, Q, 14 cm, R

Work out the size of the smallest angle in this triangle. **(3 marks)**

Use the cosine rule if you are given **three sides** and you need to find an angle. You should use this version of the cosine rule:

$$\cos A = \frac{b^2 + c^2 - a^2}{2bc}$$

Remember to check that your final answer makes sense.

Trigonometry in 3-D

You can use $S^O_H C^A_H T^O_A$ to find the angle between a LINE and a PLANE.

You might need to combine trigonometry and Pythagoras' theorem when you are solving 3-D problems.

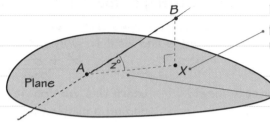

Point X is directly below point B, so ABX is a right-angled triangle.

Angle z is the angle between the line and the plane.

Worked example

Aiming higher

The diagram shows a triangular prism.

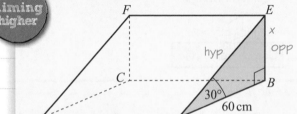

Calculate the angle between the line DE and the base of the prism.   **(6 marks)**

△ABE: you know one angle and the adjacent side. You are looking for the opposite side, so use T^O_A.

△DAB: you know two sides so you can use Pythagoras' theorem.

△DEB: you know the opposite and adjacent sides so use T^O_A. Use $\tan^{-1}$ to find the value of z.

Do **not** round any of your answers until the end — write down at least six figures from each calculator display.

$$\tan 30° = \frac{x}{60}$$
$$x = 60 \times \tan 30°$$
$$= 34.6410... \text{ cm}$$

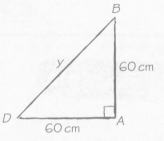

$$y^2 = 60^2 + 60^2$$
$$= 7200$$
$$y = \sqrt{7200} = 84.8528... \text{ cm}$$

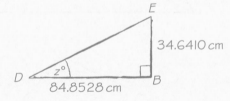

$$\tan z° = \frac{34.6410...}{84.8528...} = 0.408\,24...$$
$$z° = \tan^{-1} 0.408\,24... = 22.2076...$$
$$= 22.2° \text{ (to 3 s.f.)}$$

Now try this

Aiming higher

$ML = 28$ cm and $JK = 40$ cm

Angle $MKL = 32°$

Angles MLK, MLJ and JKL are all $90°$.

Work out the size of angle MJL.   **(6 marks)**

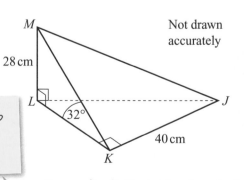

Not drawn accurately

Draw sketches of triangles MLK, LJK and MJL to keep track of your working. Remember you might need to combine trigonometry and Pythagoras' theorem.

Sectors of circles

Each pair of radii divides a circle into two sectors, a MAJOR SECTOR and a MINOR SECTOR.

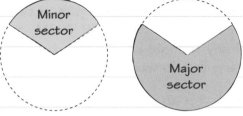

You can find the area of a sector by working out what fraction it is of the whole circle.

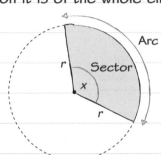

For a sector with angle x of a circle with radius r:

Sector $= \dfrac{x}{360°}$ of the whole circle so

Area of sector $= \dfrac{x}{360°} \times \pi r^2$

Arc length $= \dfrac{x}{360°} \times 2\pi r$

Learn these formulae. ✓

You can give answers in terms of π. ✓

Worked example

The diagram shows a minor sector of a circle of radius 13 cm.

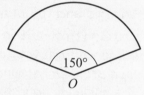

Work out the perimeter of the sector.   **(4 marks)**

Arc length $= \dfrac{x}{360°} \times 2\pi r$

$= \dfrac{150°}{360°} \times 2\pi \times 13$

$= 34.03392...$

Perimeter = arc length + radius + radius

$= 34.03392... + 13 + 13$

$= 60$ cm (2 s.f.)

Don't round until your final answer. The radius is given correct to 2 significant figures so this is a good degree of accuracy.

Finding a missing angle

You can use the formulae for arc length or area to find a missing angle in a sector. Practise this method to help you tackle the hardest questions.

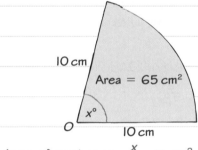

Area of sector $= \dfrac{x}{360} \times \pi r^2$

$65 = \dfrac{x}{360} \times \pi (10)^2$

$x = \dfrac{65 \times 360}{\pi (10)^2}$

$= 74.4845...$

$= 74.5°$ (to 3 s.f.)

Now try this

AB is the arc length of a minor sector of a circle, centre O, radius 12 cm.

AB measures 27 cm.

Work out the size of angle AOB, marked x on the diagram.

Give your answer correct to 3 significant figures.   **(3 marks)**

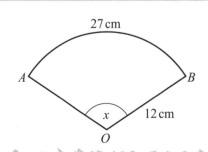

Triangles and segments

When you know the lengths of two sides and the angle BETWEEN THEM, the area of any triangle can be found using this formula:

Area = $\frac{1}{2}$ ab sin C

You can use this formula for ANY triangle. You don't need to have a right angle.

This formula is on the formula sheet.

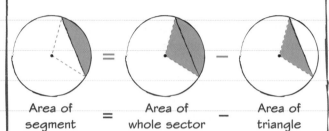

Areas of segments
A chord divides a circle into two SEGMENTS.

Area of segment = Area of whole sector − Area of triangle

Worked example

Aiming higher

The diagram shows a sector of a circle with centre O.

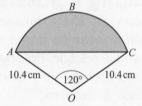

Work out the area of the shaded segment *ABC*.
Give your answer correct to 3 significant figures.   **(5 marks)**

Whole sector OABC:
Area = $\frac{120}{360}$ × π × 10.4²

= 113.2648... cm²

Triangle OAC:
Area = $\frac{1}{2}$ × 10.4 × 10.4 × sin 120°

= 46.8346... cm²

Shaded segment ABC:
Area = 113.2648... − 46.8346...

= 66.4302...

= 66.4 cm² (to 3 s.f)

If you are aiming for a top grade you need to be able to calculate the area of a sector and a triangle.

To get full marks you need to keep track of your working. Make sure you write down exactly what you are calculating at each step.

Remember that 10.4 cm is the length of one side of the triangle **and** the radius of the circle.

Make sure you don't round too soon. Write down all the figures from your calculator display at each step. Only round your **final answer** to 3 significant figures.

Which formula?
If you know the base and the vertical height:

Area = $\frac{1}{2}$ × base × vertical height
= $\frac{1}{2}$ × 6 × 2.1
= 6.3 cm²

If you know two sides and the included angle:

Area = $\frac{1}{2}$ ab sin C
= $\frac{1}{2}$ × 5 × 6 × sin 25°
= 6.3... cm²

Now try this

Aiming higher

Here is a circle, radius 4 cm, with angle *AOC* = 135°

Using the fact that sin 135° = sin 45° = $\frac{1}{\sqrt{2}}$ show clearly that the

area of the minor segment *ABC* = $6\pi − 4\sqrt{2}$ cm²   **(5 marks)**

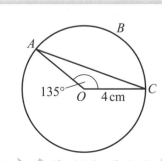

Similar shapes 2

The relationship between similar shapes is defined by a SCALE FACTOR.
A and B are similar shapes. B is an enlargement of A with scale factor k.

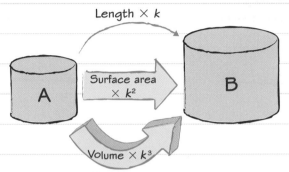

Length × k

Surface area × k^2

Volume × k^3

When a shape is enlarged by a linear scale factor k:

- Enlarged surface area
  = k^2 × original surface area
- Enlarged volume
  = k^3 × original volume
- Enlarged mass = k^3 × original mass

Worked example

Aiming higher

Here are two designs for a sticker.

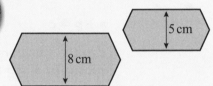

5 cm

8 cm

The two stickers are mathematically similar.
The area of the smaller sticker is 50 cm².
Calculate the area of the larger sticker.

(2 marks)

$k = \dfrac{8}{5} = 1.6$

$50 \times k^2 = 50 \times 1.6^2$

$\qquad = 50 \times 2.56$

$\qquad = 128$

Area of larger sticker = 128 cm²

EXAM ALERT!

If a 2-D shape is enlarged by a linear scale factor k, its **area** is increased by a factor of k^2.

1. Use the lengths given to work out the linear scale factor, k.

2. Multiply the area of the smaller shape by k^2 to find the area of the larger shape.

Students have struggled with exam questions similar to this – **be prepared!**

Comparing volumes

You can use k^3 to compare volume, mass or capacity.

$k = \dfrac{32}{16} = 2$

Volume of large bottle

$= 1.2 \times k^3$

$= 1.2 \times 8$

$= 9.6$ litres

1.2 litres   ←16 cm→   ←32 cm→

Now try this

Aiming higher

Here are three mathematically similar containers.
The table shows some information about these containers.

small

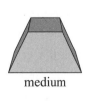
medium

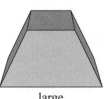
large

	Height (cm)	Area of top of container (cm²)	Volume (cm³)
small	12	85	Y
medium	36	X	7830
large	W	2125	Z

Work out the missing values, W, X, Y and Z.

(6 marks)

Vectors

This vector can be written as **a**, $\overrightarrow{AB}$ or $\binom{2}{5}$
Its DIRECTION is shown by the arrow. The length of the line segment AB is the MODULUS (or MAGNITUDE) of the vector.

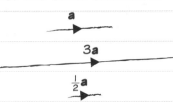

You can multiply a vector by a number. The new vector has a different magnitude but the same direction.

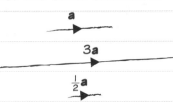

If **b** is a vector then −**b** is a vector with the same magnitude but opposite direction.

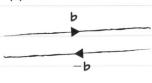

Worked example

In the diagram, *OADB* and *ACED* are parallelograms. *M* is the midpoint of *CE* and *D* is the midpoint of *BE*.

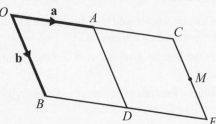

Express in terms of **a** and **b** the following vectors. Give your answers in simplest form.

(a) $\overrightarrow{OD}$ **(1 mark)**

$\overrightarrow{OD} = \overrightarrow{OA} + \overrightarrow{AD}$
$= \mathbf{a} + \mathbf{b}$

(b) $\overrightarrow{BC}$ **(2 marks)**

$\overrightarrow{BC} = \overrightarrow{BD} + \overrightarrow{DE} + \overrightarrow{EC}$
$= \mathbf{a} + \mathbf{a} - \mathbf{b} = 2\mathbf{a} - \mathbf{b}$

(c) $\overrightarrow{OM}$ **(2 marks)**

$\overrightarrow{OM} = \overrightarrow{OA} + \overrightarrow{AC} + \tfrac{1}{2}\overrightarrow{CE}$
$= \mathbf{a} + \mathbf{a} + \tfrac{1}{2}\mathbf{b} = 2\mathbf{a} + \tfrac{1}{2}\mathbf{b}$

Adding vectors

You can add vectors using the TRIANGLE LAW. You trace a path along the added vectors to find the new vector.

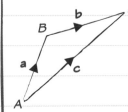

$\mathbf{a} + \mathbf{b} = \mathbf{c}$

c is the resultant vector of **a** and **b**.

$A \to B \to C$ is the same as $A \to C$

For each vector, trace a path along the shape from the start point to the end point. If you go in the **opposite** direction to the vector then you need to **subtract**. $\overrightarrow{AD} = \overrightarrow{OB}$ because they are **parallel**. There is more about this on the next page.

M is the midpoint of *CE*. This means that $\overrightarrow{CM} = \tfrac{1}{2}\overrightarrow{CE} = \tfrac{1}{2}\mathbf{b}$

Now try this

In triangle *OAB*, *M* is the midpoint of *OA*.
$AN = \tfrac{3}{4}AB$ and *P* and *Q* divide the line *OB* into three equal segments.
$\overrightarrow{OM} = \mathbf{a}$ and $\overrightarrow{OP} = \mathbf{b}$

Work out expressions for these vectors.

Give your answers in terms of **a** and **b**, in their simplest form.

(a) $\overrightarrow{OA}$ **(1 mark)** (b) $\overrightarrow{OB}$ **(1 mark)**
(c) $\overrightarrow{PM}$ **(1 mark)** (d) $\overrightarrow{AB}$ **(1 mark)**
(e) $\overrightarrow{ON}$ **(2 marks)** (f) $\overrightarrow{QN}$ **(2 marks)**

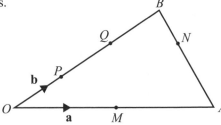

Solving vector problems

Parallel vectors

If one vector can be written as a MULTIPLE of the other then the vectors are PARALLEL.

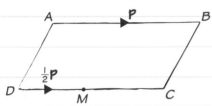

In this parallelogram M is the midpoint of DC. AB is parallel to DM so $\overrightarrow{DM} = \frac{1}{2}\overrightarrow{AB}$

Remember that AB means the line segment AB (or the length of the line segment AB). $\overrightarrow{AB}$ means the vector which takes you from A to B.

Collinear points

If three points lie on the SAME STRAIGHT LINE then they are collinear. Here are three points:

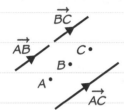

If any TWO of the vectors $\overrightarrow{AB}$, $\overrightarrow{BC}$ or $\overrightarrow{AC}$ are parallel, then the three points must be collinear.

Worked example

Aiming higher

In the diagram, OPQ is a triangle.
Point R lies on the line PQ such that
$PR:RQ = 1:2$
Point S lies on the line through OR such that
$OR:OS = 1:3$

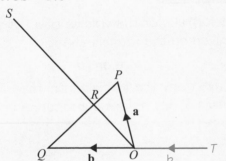

(a) Show that $\overrightarrow{OS} = 2\mathbf{a} + \mathbf{b}$ **(3 marks)**

$\overrightarrow{PQ} = -\mathbf{a} + \mathbf{b}$, so $\overrightarrow{PR} = \frac{1}{3}(-\mathbf{a} + \mathbf{b})$

$\overrightarrow{OR} = \mathbf{a} + \frac{1}{3}(-\mathbf{a} + \mathbf{b})$

$\quad\quad = \frac{1}{3}(2\mathbf{a} + \mathbf{b})$

$\overrightarrow{OS} = 3\overrightarrow{OR}$

$\quad\quad = 2\mathbf{a} + \mathbf{b}$

(b) Point T is added to the diagram such that $\overrightarrow{TO} = \mathbf{b}$. Prove that points T, P and S lie on the same straight line.   **(3 marks)**

$\overrightarrow{TP} = \mathbf{a} + \mathbf{b}$

$\overrightarrow{TS} = \mathbf{b} + 2\mathbf{a} + \mathbf{b}$

$\quad\quad = 2\mathbf{a} + 2\mathbf{b}$

$\quad\quad = 2(\mathbf{a} + \mathbf{b})$

$\overrightarrow{TS} = 2\overrightarrow{TP}$ so $\overrightarrow{TS}$ and $\overrightarrow{TP}$ are parallel. Both vectors pass through T so they lie on the same straight line.

You might be given information about the lengths of lines as ratios.

$PR:RQ = 1:2$. There are $2 + 1 = 3$ parts in this ratio. This means that R is $\frac{1}{3}$ of the way along PQ so $\overrightarrow{PR} = \frac{1}{3}\overrightarrow{PQ}$

$OR:OS = 1:3$ This means that $\overrightarrow{OS} = 3\overrightarrow{OR}$

If the question tells you another point has been added to a diagram you should always draw it on your exam paper. To show that T, P and S lie on the same straight line you need to show that **two** of the vectors $\overrightarrow{TP}$, $\overrightarrow{TS}$ and $\overrightarrow{PS}$ are parallel.

Now try this

Aiming higher

In triangle OAB, M is the midpoint of OA.

$OH = HJ = JK = KB$

S and T divide the line AB into three equal segments. $\overrightarrow{OM} = \mathbf{a}$ and $\overrightarrow{OH} = \mathbf{b}$

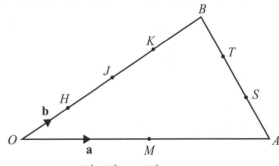

(a) Prove that $\overrightarrow{HA}$, $\overrightarrow{JS}$ and $\overrightarrow{KT}$ are all parallel.   **(6 marks)**

(b) State the ratio $KT:JS:HA$ **(1 mark)**

Problem-solving practice

Problem-solving skills are essential to success in your International GCSE exam. Practise using the questions on the next two pages.

For these questions you might need to:

- choose which mathematical technique or skill to use
- apply a technique in a new context
- plan your strategy to solve a longer problem
- show your working clearly and give reasons for your answers.

1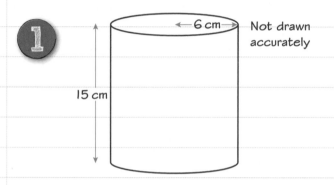

6 cm   Not drawn accurately

15 cm

Jenny fills some empty flowerpots completely with compost.

Each flowerpot is in the shape of a cylinder of height 15 cm and radius 6 cm.

Jenny has a 15 litre bag of compost.

She fills up each flowerpot completely.

How many flowerpots can she fill completely?

You must show your working. **(4 marks)**

Circles and cylinders p. 64

You need to remember that
1 litre = 1000 cm³

You are trying to work out how many flowerpots Jenny can fill **completely** so you'll need to round your final answer **down**.

TOP TIP

The formula for the volume of a cylinder is given on the formula sheet:

$$V = \pi r^2 h$$

Always copy the formula from the formula sheet before substituting in any values.

2 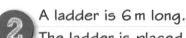A ladder is 6 m long.

The ladder is placed on horizontal ground, resting against a vertical wall.

The instructions for using the ladder say that the bottom of the ladder must not be closer than 1.5 m to the bottom of the wall.

How far up the wall can the ladder reach if the instructions are followed?

(3 marks)

Pythagoras' theorem p. 66

You should definitely draw a sketch to show the information in the question.

TOP TIP

Be careful when you are working out the length of a **short** side using Pythagoras' theorem.

Remember: short² + short² = long²

short² = long² − short²

Problem-solving practice

3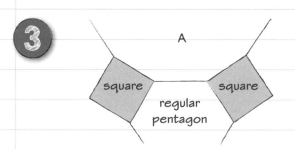

The diagram shows 2 squares, part of a regular pentagon and part of a regular *n*-sided polygon, A.

Calculate the value of *n*. Show your working clearly.   (5 marks)

Angles in polygons p. 58

Follow these steps:

1. Work out the interior angles of a regular pentagon and a square.
2. Use the fact that the angles around a point add up to 360° to find the interior angle of A.
3. Subtract this from 180° to find the exterior angle of A.
4. Divide 360° by this to work out *n*.

TOP TIP

If there are a lot of steps in a question it's a good idea to **plan** your answer before you start.

4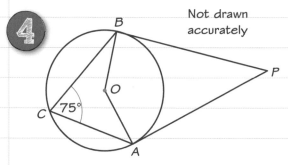

In the diagram A, B and C are points on the circumference of a circle with centre O.

PA and *PB* are tangents to the circle.

Angle *ACB* = 75°

Work out the size of angle *APB*. Show your working clearly.   (4 marks)

Circle theorems p. 60
Circle facts p. 59

Aiming higher

You have to write down a reason for **each step** of your working. These are some of the reasons you could use to answer this question:

- Angle at the centre of a circle is twice the angle at the circumference.
- Angle between a tangent and a radius is 90°.
- Angles in a quadrilateral add up to 360°.

TOP TIP

When you are learning circle theorems, draw a sketch to explain each one. This will help you to spot which theorem to use in an exam question.

5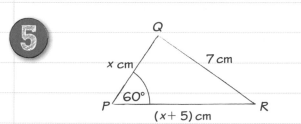

The diagram shows the lengths of the sides of triangle PQR. Angle *QPR* = 60°

(a) Show that $x^2 + 5x - 24 = 0$

          (3 marks)

(b) Find the value of *x*.   (3 marks)

Quadratic equations p. 35
The cosine rule p. 81

Aiming higher

Use the cosine rule to write an equation, then solve it to find *x*. The question says "Show that..." so you need to show all your working. Even though the cosine rule is given on the formula sheet, you should still copy it down before you substitute.

TOP TIP

The question only asks for one value of *x*. If you have to solve a quadratic equation in a practical situation, make sure you choose the solution that makes sense.

Mean, median and mode

You can analyse data by calculating statistics like the MEAN, MEDIAN and MODE.

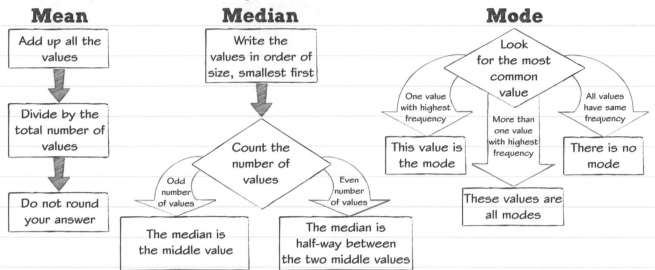

Mean
Add up all the values → Divide by the total number of values → Do not round your answer

Median
Write the values in order of size, smallest first → Count the number of values
- Odd number of values → The median is the middle value
- Even number of values → The median is half-way between the two middle values

Mode
Look for the most common value
- One value with highest frequency → This value is the mode
- More than one value with highest frequency → These values are all modes
- All values have same frequency → There is no mode

Worked example

Kayla has 8 numbered cards.

1 2 3 4 5 6 7 8

She removes two cards. The mean value of the remaining cards is 4.

Which two cards could Kayla have removed? Give **one** possible answer.

(4 marks)

6 × 4 = 24
1 + 2 + 3 + 4 + 5 + 6 + 7 + 8 = 36
36 − 24 = 12
The removed cards add up to 12 so Kayla could have removed 7 and 5
Check:
$$\frac{1 + 2 + 3 + 4 + 6 + 8}{6} = 4 ✓$$

You can work out the sum of the 6 remaining cards using this formula:

Sum of values = mean × number of values

Subtract this sum from the sum of all 8 cards. This tells you the sum of the 2 cards Kayla removed. The removed cards were either 5 and 7 or 8 and 4.

Check it!
Work out the mean of the remaining 6 cards.

Which average works best?

	👍	👎
Mean	Uses all the data	Affected by extreme values
Median	Not affected by extreme values	Value may not exist
Mode	Suitable for data that can be described in words	Not always near the middle of the data

---

Now try this

Joe scored these marks out of 20 in **six** Maths tests.

    11   9   5   13   15   12

How many marks must he score in the next test so that his mean mark and his median mark are the same?

(3 marks)

Make sure you check your answer by calculating the new mean and median. Remember that the median is not affected by extreme values.

Frequency table averages

Finding averages from frequency tables and frequency polygons is a common exam question. This frequency table shows the numbers of pets owned by the students in a class.

The mode is I. This value has the highest frequency.

Number of pets (x)	Frequency (f)	Frequency × number of pets (f × x)
0	12	12 × 0 = 0
1	18	18 × 1 = 18
2	5	5 × 2 = 10
3	2	2 × 3 = 6
Total	37	34

To calculate the mean you need to add a column for 'f × x'.

There are 37 values so the median is the $\frac{37+1}{2}$ = 19th value.

The first 12 values are all 0. The next 18 values are 1. So the median is 1.

The total in the 'f × x' column represents the total number of pets owned by the class.

$$\text{Mean} = \frac{\text{total number of pets}}{\text{total frequency}} = \frac{34}{37} = 0.92 \text{ (to 2 d.p.)}$$

Worked example

Maisie recorded the times, in minutes, taken by 150 students to travel to school.

The table shows her results.

Time (t minutes)	Frequency (f)	Midpoint (x)	f × x
$0 \leqslant t < 20$	65	10	65 × 10 = 650
$20 \leqslant t < 30$	40	25	40 × 25 = 1000
$30 \leqslant t < 40$	39	35	39 × 35 = 1365
$40 \leqslant t < 60$	6	50	6 × 50 = 300

Total frequency = 150   Total of f × x = 3315

Everything in red is part of the answer.

(a) Work out an estimate for the mean number of minutes that the students took to travel to school.

(4 marks)

$$\frac{3315}{150} = 22.1$$

(b) Explain why your answer to part (a) is an estimate.

(1 mark)

Because you don't know the exact data values.

EXAM ALERT!

Add extra columns to the table for 'Midpoint (x)' and 'Midpoint × frequency (f × x)'.

$$\text{Estimate of mean} = \frac{\text{Total of } fx \text{ column}}{\text{Total frequency}}$$

Students have struggled with exam questions similar to this – **be prepared!**

Now try this

The table shows the ages of 120 people in a small village.

Work out an estimate of the mean age of these 120 people.   **(4 marks)**

Age, x (years)	Frequency
$0 < x \leqslant 20$	33
$20 < x \leqslant 40$	27
$40 < x \leqslant 70$	39
$70 < x \leqslant 100$	21

Interquartile range

Range and interquartile range are measures of spread. They tell you how spread out data is.
QUARTILES divide a data set into four equal parts.

Half of the values lie between the lower quartile and the upper quartile.

$Q_1 = \dfrac{n+1}{4}$th value, where n = number of data values.

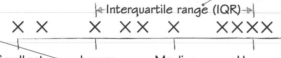

|←—Interquartile range (IQR)—→|

X X   X X X X   X X X X   X DATA VALUES

Smallest value   Lower quartile (Q_1)   Median (Q_2)   Upper quartile (Q_3)   Largest value

$Q_3 = \dfrac{3(n+1)}{4}$th value.

RANGE = largest value − smallest value

INTERQUARTILE RANGE (IQR) = upper quartile (Q_3) − lower quartile (Q_1)

Worked example

Alison recorded the heights, in cm, of some tree saplings. She put the heights in order.

21 23 23 25 26 26 31 32
33 35 36 40 40 41 42 45

Work out the interquartile range of Alison's data. **(3 marks)**

$n = 16$

$\dfrac{n+1}{4} = \dfrac{16+1}{4} = 4.25$

Q_1 = Mean of 4th and 5th values = 25.5 cm

$\dfrac{3(n+1)}{4} = \dfrac{3(16+1)}{4} = 12.75$

Q_3 = Mean of 12th and 13th values = 40 cm

IQR = $Q_3 - Q_1$ = 40 − 25.5 = 14.5 cm

1. Check that the data is arranged in order of size.

2. Find the $\dfrac{n+1}{4}$th data value. If $\dfrac{n+1}{4}$ is not a whole number, use the **mean** of the two values on either side. This is the lower quartile (Q_1).

3. Find the $\dfrac{3(n+1)}{4}$th data value, or the mean of the values on either side. This is the upper quartile (Q_3).

4. Subtract the lower quartile from the upper quartile to find the interquartile range.

Comparing distributions

You can use averages like the MEAN or MEDIAN and measures of spread like the RANGE and INTERQUARTILE RANGE to compare two sets of data. Follow these steps:

 Calculate an average and a measure of spread for both data sets.

 Write a sentence for each statistic COMPARING the values for each data set.

 Only make a statement if you can back it up with STATISTICAL EVIDENCE.

Now try this

The number of driving lessons taken by students before passing their tests are shown for two different driving instructors:

Instructor A (19 students)
23 14 10 16 34 21 19   8   14 15
16 31 20 23 45 28 18 19 20

Instructor B (27 students)
Median: 25
Interquartile range: 8

(a) Work out the median and interquartile range for Instructor A.   **(5 marks)**

(b) Make **two** comments comparing the number of lessons taken by students of each instructor.   **(2 marks)**

Frequency polygons

You can represent grouped data using a FREQUENCY POLYGON. Look at this example.

Reaction time (r milliseconds)	Frequency
$100 \leqslant r < 200$	7
$200 \leqslant r < 300$	15
$300 \leqslant r < 400$	10

Join the points with STRAIGHT LINES. Make sure you use a ruler.

Plot points at the MIDPOINT of each class interval.

This frequency polygon shows the reaction times of a class of students.

You always record FREQUENCY on the vertical axis.

If you draw a histogram on the same graph the frequency polygon joins together the midpoints of the tops of the bars.

Worked example

30 students timed how long it took them to complete a jigsaw puzzle.
The results were recorded in a grouped frequency table:

Time (t minutes)	Frequency	Midpoint
$10 \leqslant t < 14$	2	12
$14 \leqslant t < 18$	5	16
$18 \leqslant t < 22$	12	20
$22 \leqslant t < 26$	8	24
$26 \leqslant t < 30$	3	28

Show this information on a frequency polygon. **(3 marks)**

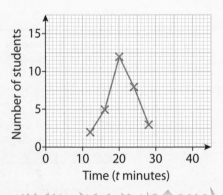

EXAM ALERT!

Start by working out the midpoints of the class intervals.

The midpoint of the class interval $10 \leqslant t < 14$
is $\dfrac{10 + 14}{2} = 12$

Check it!
In your exam you will only be asked to draw a frequency polygon for data with **equal class intervals**. So make sure that your midpoints are the same distance apart.

Students have struggled with exam questions similar to this – **be prepared!**

Estimating the mean

You can estimate the mean for data given in a frequency polygon using this formula:

$$\text{Mean} \approx \frac{\text{Sum of (midpoint} \times \text{frequency)}}{\text{Total frequency}}$$

For the worked example on the left:

$$\frac{(2 \times 12) + (5 \times 16) + (12 \times 20) + (8 \times 24) + (3 \times 28)}{30} = 20.6666...$$

An estimate for the mean time is 20 minutes, 40 seconds.

There is more about estimating the mean of grouped data on page 91.

Now try this

This table shows the times taken, in minutes, for 50 people to solve a crossword puzzle.

(a) Draw a frequency polygon for this data.
          (3 marks)

(b) Which interval contains the median time?
          (1 mark)

Time, t (minutes)	Frequency
$0 < t \leqslant 10$	3
$10 < t \leqslant 20$	9
$20 < t \leqslant 30$	11
$30 < t \leqslant 40$	18
$40 < t \leqslant 50$	7
$50 < t \leqslant 60$	2

Had a look ☐ Nearly there ☐ Nailed it! ☐

Histograms

Histograms are a good way to represent grouped data with DIFFERENT class widths.

Worked example *Aiming higher*

This table shows the finishing times in minutes of runners in a cross-country race.

Time (t minutes)	Frequency	Frequency density
$16 \leq t < 20$	12	3
$20 \leq t < 30$	45	4.5
$30 \leq t < 50$	28	1.4

Draw a histogram to represent the data.

(3 marks)

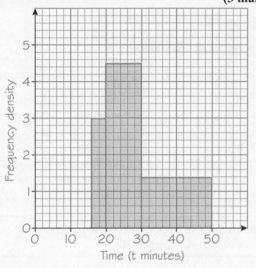

Histogram facts

No gaps between the bars. ✓

AREA of each bar is proportional to frequency. ✓

Vertical axis is labelled 'Frequency density'. ✓

Bars can be different widths. ✓

Frequency density = $\dfrac{\text{frequency}}{\text{class width}}$ ✓

The class widths in the frequency table are **different widths** so a histogram is the most suitable graph to draw.

1. Calculate the frequency densities.

$\dfrac{12}{4} = 3$ $\dfrac{45}{10} = 4.5$ $\dfrac{28}{20} = 1.4$

2. Add these values to the table as an extra column.

3. Label the vertical axis 'Frequency density'.

4. Choose a scale for the vertical axis and draw each bar.

Area and estimation

You can use the area under a histogram to estimate frequencies. An estimate for the NUMBER of maggots between 1 mm and 2 mm long is:

$0.5 \times 22 + 0.5 \times 6 = 14$

You might need to answer proportion questions about histograms in your exam. The total frequency is:

$1 \times 14 + 0.5 \times 22 + 1.5 \times 6 = 34$

So an estimate for the PROPORTION of maggots between 1 mm and 2 mm long is: $\dfrac{14}{34} = 0.4117...$ or 41% (2 s.f.)

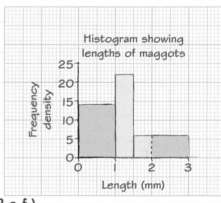

Now try this *Aiming higher*

A speed camera recorded the speed of some vehicles on a motorway. The table on the right shows the results.

(a) On graph paper, draw a histogram to illustrate this data.

(3 marks)

(b) Estimate the proportion of vehicles travelling at more than 65 mph. **(2 marks)**

Speed, s (mph)	Frequency
$0 < s \leq 40$	48
$40 < s \leq 50$	32
$50 < s \leq 70$	128
$70 < s \leq 80$	88
$80 < s \leq 110$	24

Cumulative frequency

In your exam you might have to draw a cumulative frequency graph, or use one to find the median or the interquartile range.

How to draw a cumulative frequency graph

Reaction time t (s)	Frequency	Cumulative frequency
$0 < t \leqslant 0.1$	2	2
$0.1 < t \leqslant 0.2$	5	$2 + 5 = 7$
$0.2 < t \leqslant 0.3$	18	$7 + 18 = 25$
$0.3 < t \leqslant 0.4$	5	$25 + 5 = 30$
$0.4 < t \leqslant 0.5$	1	$30 + 1 = 31$

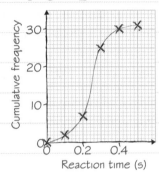

1. Plot 0 at the beginning of the first class interval.

2. Plot each value at the UPPER end of its class interval.

3. Join your points with a SMOOTH CURVE.

Add a column for CUMULATIVE FREQUENCY to your frequency table.

Check that your final value is the same as the total frequency.

Here's another example:

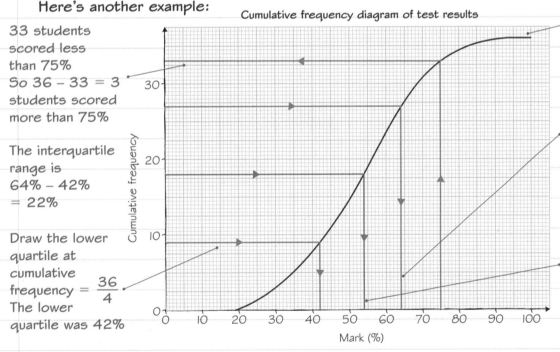

Cumulative frequency diagram of test results

33 students scored less than 75%
So 36 – 33 = 3 students scored more than 75%

There were 36 students in the class. (This is the FIRST FACT you should establish.)

The interquartile range is 64% – 42% = 22%

Draw the upper quartile at cumulative frequency = $3 \times \dfrac{36}{4}$
The upper quartile was 64%

Draw the lower quartile at cumulative frequency = $\dfrac{36}{4}$
The lower quartile was 42%

Draw the median at cumulative frequency = $\dfrac{36}{2}$
The median was 54%

Now try this

Here is a cumulative frequency graph for the journey times to college of 500 students.

Use the graph to find an estimate for

(a) the median journey time. **(1 mark)**

(b) the interquartile range of the journey times. **(2 marks)**

(c) the percentage of students who took more than 44 minutes to travel to college. **(2 marks)**

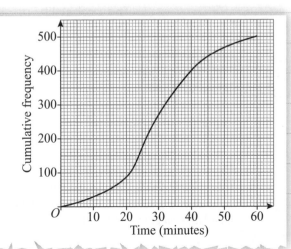

Probability 1

For EQUALLY LIKELY OUTCOMES the probability (P) that something will happen is:

$$\text{Probability} = \frac{\text{number of successful outcomes}}{\text{total number of possible outcomes}}$$

If you know the probability that an event WILL happen, you can calculate the probability that it won't happen:

P(Event doesn't happen) = 1 − P(Event happens)

 The probability of rolling a 6 on a normal fair dice is $\frac{1}{6}$. So the probability of NOT rolling a 6 is $1 - \frac{1}{6} = \frac{5}{6}$

Add or multiply?

Events are MUTUALLY EXCLUSIVE if they can't BOTH happen at the same time. For mutually exclusive events:

P(A or B) = P(A) + P(B)

Events are INDEPENDENT if the outcome of one doesn't affect the outcome of the other. For independent events:

P(A and B) = P(A) × P(B)

Worked example

Amir designs a game for his school fete. This table shows the probability of winning a prize:

Prize	Badge	Keyring	Cuddly toy
Probability	0.35	0.18	0.07

(a) What is the probability of **not** winning a prize? **(2 marks)**

P(Win) = 0.35 + 0.18 + 0.07 = 0.6

P(Not win) = 1 − 0.6 = 0.4

(b) Amir plays the game three times. What is the probability that he does not win a prize? **(2 marks)**

0.4 × 0.4 × 0.4 = 0.064

(a) To work out the probability of winning **any** prize you need to add together the probabilities. Then you can use this rule to work out the probability of not winning a prize:

$$P\binom{\text{NOT winning}}{\text{a prize}} = 1 - P\binom{\text{Winning a}}{\text{prize}}$$

(b) To work out the probability of Amir not winning on any of his three games, you need to multiply the probabilities.

Sample space diagrams

First coin

	H	T
H	HH	TH
T	HT	TT

Second coin

A SAMPLE SPACE DIAGRAM shows you all the possible outcomes of an event. Here are all the possible outcomes when two coins are flipped.

- There are four possible outcomes. TH means getting a tail on the first coin and a head on the second coin.
- The probability of getting two tails when two coins are flipped is $\frac{1}{4}$ or 0.25. There are 4 possible outcomes and only 1 successful outcome (TT).

Now try this

A spinner has four colours. This table shows the probability of landing on each colour.

Colour	Red	Blue	Green	Yellow
Probability	0.1		0.2	0.1

(a) What is the probability of landing on blue? **(2 marks)**

(b) What is the probability of not landing on red? **(1 mark)**

(c) The spinner is spun twice. What is the probability that it lands on blue both times? **(2 marks)**

Each spin is an independent event so you can multiply the probabilities.

Probability 2

You need to be able to calculate probabilities for data given in graphs and tables. You can use this formula to estimate a probability from a frequency table:

$$\text{Probability} = \frac{\text{frequency of outcome}}{\text{total frequency}}$$

This is called RELATIVE FREQUENCY.

Golden rule

Probability estimates based on relative frequency are MORE ACCURATE for larger samples (or for more trials in an experiment).

In the sample there were 15 + 10 = 25 eggs which weighed 55 g or more. So an estimate for the probability of picking an egg which weighs 55 g or more is $\frac{25}{40}$ or $\frac{5}{8}$

When you are calculating probabilities you can give your answers as decimals or fractions in lowest terms.

Worked example

An egg farm weighed a sample of 40 eggs. It recorded the results in a frequency table:

Weight, w (g)	Frequency
$45 \leqslant w < 50$	6
$50 \leqslant w < 55$	9
$55 \leqslant w < 60$	15
$60 \leqslant w < 65$	10

(a) Roselle buys some eggs from the farm and picks one at random. Estimate the probability that the egg weighs 55 g or more. **(2 marks)**

$$15 + 10 = 25$$

$$P(w \geqslant 55) \approx \frac{25}{40} = \frac{5}{8}$$

So the probability is $\frac{5}{8}$

(b) Comment on the accuracy of your estimate. **(1 mark)**

40 is a fairly small sample size, so the estimate is not very accurate.

Expectation

Probability theory helps you predict the outcome of an event.

If you flip a coin 100 times, you can expect to get heads about 50 times. You probably won't get heads exactly 50 times, but it's a good guess.

$$\text{Expected frequency} = \text{number of trials} \times \text{probability}$$

Worked example

The probability of a biased coin landing heads up is 0.4

The coin is flipped 300 times.

Work out an estimate for the number of times the coin will land heads up.

$$300 \times 0.4 = 120$$

Now try this

In a school, the probability that a girl is left-handed is 0.15

The probability that a boy is left-handed is 0.2

The school has 420 girls and 390 boys.

(a) Estimate the number of left-handed students in the school. **(3 marks)**

(b) A student is picked at random from the whole school.
Estimate the probability that the student is left-handed. **(1 mark)**

An estimate for the number of left-handed **girls** is 420 × 0.15

97

Tree diagrams

A tree diagram shows all the possible outcomes from a series of events and their probabilities.

This is a tree diagram for Holly's journey to school.

You write the probability for each event on the branch.

At each branch the probabilities add up to 1.
$$\frac{2}{3} + \frac{1}{3} = 1$$

The outcome of the first event can affect the probability of the second.

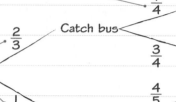

You write the outcomes at the ends of the branches.
You can use shorthand like this.

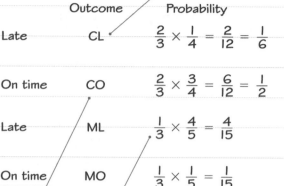

Outcome	Probability
CL	$\frac{2}{3} \times \frac{1}{4} = \frac{2}{12} = \frac{1}{6}$
CO	$\frac{2}{3} \times \frac{3}{4} = \frac{6}{12} = \frac{1}{2}$
ML	$\frac{1}{3} \times \frac{4}{5} = \frac{4}{15}$
MO	$\frac{1}{3} \times \frac{1}{5} = \frac{1}{15}$

Holly is less likely to be on time if she misses the bus.

Each branch is like a different parallel universe. In this universe, Holly catches the bus and gets to school on time.

You multiply along the branches to find the probability of each outcome.

The probability that Holly misses the bus and is late for school is $\frac{4}{15}$

Golden rules

 1 Look out for the words REPLACE or PUT BACK in a probability question.

WITH replacement: probabilities stay the same.

WITHOUT replacement: first probability stays the same while the others change.

2  MULTIPLY ALONG THE BRANCHES — ADD UP THE OUTCOMES

Worked example

 Aiming higher

There are 3 strawberry yoghurts and 4 pineapple yoghurts in a fridge. Noah picks two yoghurts at random from the fridge. Work out the probability that both the yoghurts were the same flavour.

(4 marks)

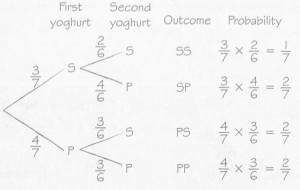

P (both yoghurts same flavour) = P(SS) + P(PP)
$$= \frac{1}{7} + \frac{2}{7} = \frac{3}{7}$$

This is an example of selection **without replacement**. The two events are not independent. The probabilities for the second pick change depending on which flavour yoghurt was picked first. A tree diagram is the **safest** way to answer questions like this.

Now try this

Aiming higher

Grace buys a packet of 12 tulip bulbs. They all look the same, but 7 of them will produce red flowers and 5 will produce yellow flowers.

A bulb is taken at random and planted.

A second bulb is taken at random and planted. Work out the probability that the two bulbs produce **different** coloured flowers. **(4 marks)**

Problem-solving practice

Problem-solving skills are essential to success in your International GCSE exam.

Practise using the questions on the next two pages.

For these questions you might need to:

- choose which mathematical technique or skill to use
- apply a technique in a new context
- plan your strategy to solve a longer problem
- show your working clearly and give reasons for your answers.

---

1 Eight numbers have a mean of 12.
The numbers are

7   4   17   20 x 9   6   2x

Work out the value of x.   (4 marks)

Mean, median and mode p. 90

There are 8 values and the mean is 12.
This means that the sum of the data values is
$8 \times 12 = 96$

You know that all the values, including x and $2x$ must add up to 96. Use this information to write an equation and solve it to find x.

TOP TIP

You can solve lots of problems involving the mean using:

Sum of values = mean $\times$ number of values

---

2 Rania measured the reaction times of her fellow students using a computer program. This frequency polygon shows her result.

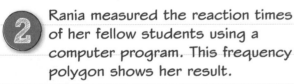

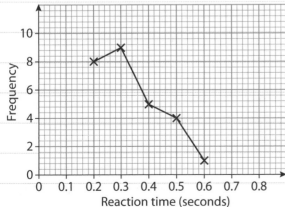

Frequency table averages p. 91

Frequency polygons are usually used to represent **grouped continuous data**. In a frequency polygon the values are plotted at the **midpoints** of the class intervals, so you have less work to do when estimating the mean.

TOP TIP

Make sure you can read and work with data represented in a table, a graph or as a list of numbers. In your exam you might be given data in any of these formats.

Calculate an estimate of the mean reaction time.   (3 marks)

Problem-solving practice

3 The weights in grams of the lemons in a box of lemons from Sunvale Farm are given in order below.

77 77 79 80 82 82 83 85
85 87 89 91 91 92 95

This table summarises the weights of the lemons in a box from Greentree Farm.

Median	84 grams
Interquartile range	6 grams

Compare the weights of the lemons in each box.   (5 marks)

Interquartile range p. 92

You need to calculate both of these statistics for the box from Sunvale Farm. There are 15 lemons in the box:

Lower quartile $= \dfrac{15 + 1}{4} =$ 4th value

Upper quartile $= \dfrac{3(15 + 1)}{4} =$ 12th value

TOP TIP

When comparing data make sure you calculate the **same** statistics for each data set, and support all your statements with **statistical evidence**.

---

4 Beccy has two bags of numbered balls.

Bag A   Bag B

She chooses a ball at random from bag A and places it in bag B. Then she chooses a ball at random from bag B and places it in bag A.

Calculate the probability that the sum of the balls in bag A will be 18 or greater.   (4 marks)

Probability 1 p. 96

Aiming higher

Work out all the ways Beccy can end up with a total of 18 or more in bag A.
Use a table to keep track of your working:

Work out the probability of each outcome and add them together.

A → B	B → A	Total in A
1	4	18
1	5	19
2	5	18

You can answer lots of tricky probability questions by writing down all the successful outcomes then working out the probability of each one.

---

5 In a board game, Diego picks a question card. He can pick an easy (E), medium (M) or hard (H) question.

The probabilities of picking each type of question are 0.54, 0.31 and 0.15 respectively.

The probabilities that he gets each type of question correct are 0.8, 0.5 and 0.1 respectively.

Work out the probability that Diego gets his question correct.   (5 marks)

Tree diagrams p. 98

Aiming higher

Either draw a tree diagram, or write down the successful outcomes and work out their probabilities. For example:

P(E, correct) $= 0.54 \times 0.8 = 0.432$

TOP TIP

If you draw a tree diagram for a conditional probability question you will probably get some or all of the marks for this question because you won't leave out any of the possibilities.

Formulae page

Volume of a prism = area of cross section × length

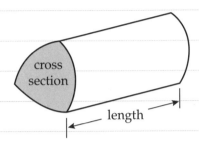

Area of trapezium = $\frac{1}{2}(a + b)h$

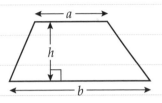

Volume of sphere = $\frac{4}{3}\pi r^3$

Surface area of sphere = $4\pi r^2$

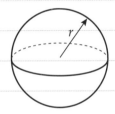

Volume of cone = $\frac{1}{3}\pi r^2 h$

Curved surface area of cone = $\pi r l$

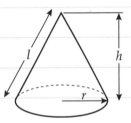

In any triangle ABC

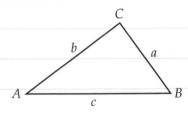

Sine Rule $\dfrac{a}{\sin A} = \dfrac{b}{\sin B} = \dfrac{c}{\sin C}$

Cosine Rule $a^2 = b^2 + c^2 - 2bc\cos A$

Area of triangle = $\frac{1}{2}ab\sin C$

The Quadratic Equation

The solutions of $ax^2 + bx + c = 0$
where $a \neq 0$, are given by

$$x = \frac{-b \pm \sqrt{(b^2 - 4ac)}}{2a}$$

Answers

1. Calculator skills 1

1 86.3%

2 Aisha: \$557.50; Joshua: \$540; Aisha spends the most on rent.

2. Factors and primes

1 (a) $980 = 2^2 \times 5 \times 7^2$ (b) 28

2 63

3. Indices 1

1 (a) 7^8 (b) $n = 3$

2 $k = 2$

3 (a) (i) 2^4 (ii) 7^{12} (iii) 5^2 (b) $n = 11$

4. Indices 2

1 (a) 7^{h-k} (b) 7^{2h} (c) 7^{h+2k}

2 $n = -3$

3 $\sqrt{\dfrac{49}{7^3}} = \sqrt{\dfrac{7^2}{7^3}} = \sqrt{7^{-1}} = 7^{-\frac{1}{2}}$

5. Calculator skills 2

(a) 4.197530864 (b) 4.20 (3 s.f.)

6. Fractions

1 (a) $\dfrac{7}{10} - \dfrac{1}{4} = \dfrac{14}{20} - \dfrac{5}{20}$
$= \dfrac{9}{20}$

(b) $3\dfrac{4}{9} + 1\dfrac{5}{6} = \dfrac{31}{9} + \dfrac{11}{6}$
$= \dfrac{62}{18} + \dfrac{33}{18}$
$= \dfrac{95}{18}$
$= 5\dfrac{5}{18}$

2 (a) $\dfrac{3}{4} \div \dfrac{5}{12} = \dfrac{3}{4} \times \dfrac{12}{5}$
$= \dfrac{9}{5}$
$= 1\dfrac{4}{5}$

(b) $1\dfrac{7}{8} \times 2\dfrac{2}{3} = \dfrac{15}{8} \times \dfrac{8}{3}$
$= 5$

7. Standard form

(a) 277 000 (b) 5.511×10^5 kg

8. Percentage change

1 £14 310

2 34.6%

9. Reverse percentages and compound interest

1 £45

2 202 000 (3 s.f.)

10. Recurring decimals

1 Let $n = 0.018181818\ldots$
$100n = 1.818181818\ldots$
$99n = 1.8$
$n = \dfrac{1.8}{99} = \dfrac{1}{55}$

2 Let $n = 0.351351351\ldots$
$1000n = 351.351351351\ldots$
$999n = 351$
$n = \dfrac{351}{999} = \dfrac{13}{37}$

11. Ratio

1 £161

2 (a) 21 (b) 24

12. Proportion

(a) 275 g (b) 20

13. Upper and lower bounds

1 LB for width = LB for area ÷ UB for length
$= 315 \div 22.5$
$= 14$ cm

2 13.5 m²

14. Surds 1

1 $\sqrt{32} + \sqrt{98} = \sqrt{16 \times 2} + \sqrt{49 \times 2}$
$= 4\sqrt{2} + 7\sqrt{2}$
$= 11\sqrt{2}$
$p = 11$

2 $\dfrac{35}{\sqrt{7}} = \dfrac{35\sqrt{7}}{7} = 5\sqrt{7}$

3 $x = 32$

15. Set notation

1 (a) $P \cap Q = \{e, i, c\}$ (b) $P \cup Q = \{m, e, t, r, i, c, g, s\}$

2 (a) No. $A \cap B = \{2, 5\}$ (b) $n(A \cap B) = 2$

16. Venn diagrams

1
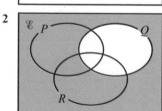

2
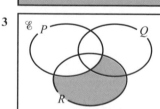

3
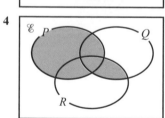

4

17. Problem-solving with sets

27 tables ordered naan bread but not roti bread

18-19. Problem-solving practice

1 312 students

2 (a) For example, {5, 9, 13} (b) For example, {13, 15, 17}

3 24.72 litres

4 (a) 2×10^n (b) $1.6 \times 10^{4m+1}$

5 $n = 4$

6 178 cm (3 s.f.)

20. Algebraic expressions

1 h^{12}

2 (a) $16a^{20}b^4$ (b) $15x^7y^9$ (c) $3d^6g^5$

3 $5p^3$

21. Expanding brackets

1 $5a - 30$

2 (a) $2b - 11$ (b) $24y^4 + 32y$

    (c) $2x^3 + 3x^2 - 3x$ (d) $m^2 + 6m - 27$

3 (a) $6g^2 - 23ge + 20e^2$ (b) $16x^2 + 56x + 49$

22. Factorising

1 (a) $2(2a - 3)$ (b) $y(y + 5)$

2 (a) $3g(4 + g)$ (b) $(p - 14)(p - 1)$

    (c) $2x(3x - 4y)$

3 (a) $4ma(1 - 6m)$ (b) $(p + 8)(p - 8)$

4 (a) $(3y - 5)(y + 4)$ (b) $(x + 9y)(x - 9y)$

    (c) $2(5g + e)(5g - e)$

23. Algebraic fractions

1 (a) $\dfrac{2a + 9}{6a}$ (b) $\dfrac{1}{y - 3}$

2 (a) $\dfrac{x(x - 2)}{x + 5}$ (b) $\dfrac{m - 6}{3m^2}$

24. Surds 2

1 $(3 - \sqrt{12})^2 = (3 - \sqrt{12})(3 - \sqrt{12})$

    $= 9 - 3\sqrt{12} - 3\sqrt{12} + (\sqrt{12})^2$

    $= 21 - 6\sqrt{12}$

    $= 21 - 6 \times 2\sqrt{3}$

    $= 21 - 12\sqrt{3}$

2 $x = 3$ and $k = 8$

25. Straight-line graphs

(a) $\frac{2}{3}$ (b) $y = \frac{2}{3}x - 3$

26. Parallel lines

1 (a) $(4, 1)$ (b) $y = -\frac{1}{2}x + 3$

2 (a) $\frac{1}{4}$ (b) $y = \frac{1}{4}x + 1$ (c) $y = \frac{1}{4}x$

27. Formulae

21.9 cm

28. Linear equations 1

1 (a) $w = 7$ (b) $x = -1$

2 (a) $y = -\frac{7}{4}$ (b) $m = 4$

29. Linear equations 2

1 (a) $w = -5$ (b) $x = 3$

2 (a) $y = 6$ (b) $m = 37$

30. Rearranging formulae

1 $t = \dfrac{4p + 1}{3}$

2 $w = \dfrac{m^2 - 7}{5}$

2 $y = \dfrac{5 - 2x}{x + 9}$

31. Inequalities

1 $-2, -1, 0, 1, 2$

2 $-4, -3, -2, -1, 0$

3 $n > -2$

4 $n \geqslant 22$

32. Inequalities on graphs

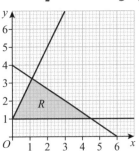

33. Quadratic graphs

(a)

x	-2	-1	0	1	2	3	4
y	4	-1	-4	-5	-4	-1	4

(b), (c)

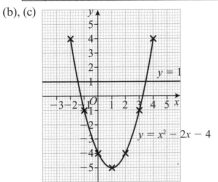

(d) From $(-1.5, 1)$ to $(-1.4, 1)$ **and** from $(3.4, 1)$ to $(3.5, 1)$

34. Simultaneous equations 1

1 $x = 5, y = 1.5$

2 $x = 4, y = -1$

35. Quadratic equations

(a) $m = 6, m = 2$ (b) $w = -4, w = 9$

(c) $y = \frac{3}{5}, y = -8$ (d) $x = \frac{5}{7}, x = -1$

36. The quadratic formula

1 $x = -1.16, x = 0.736$ (3 s.f.)

2 $m = -106, m = 56.4$ (3 s.f.)

37. Quadratics and fractions

1 $x = \frac{3}{4}, x = -3$

2 $x = -\frac{15}{2}, x = -4$

38. Using quadratic graphs

(a)

x	-5	-4	-3	-2	-1	0	1	2
y	7	1	-3	-5	-5	-3	1	7

(b)

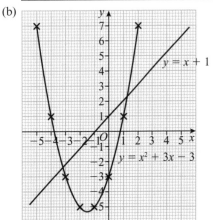

(c) -3.8 and 0.8 (d) $y = x + 1$, $x = 1.2$ and -3.2

ANSWERS

39. Drawing harder graphs

(a)
x	0.1	0.2	0.5	1	1.5	2	3	4
y	10.0	5.0	2.3	2	2.9	4.5	9.3	16.3

(b)
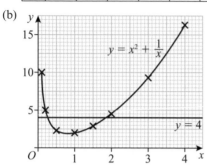

(c) $x = 0.2$ or 0.3, $x = 1.8$ or 1.9

40. Quadratic inequalities

1 $-2 < p < 2$

2 $x \geqslant 8$ or $x \leqslant -8$

41. Simultaneous equations 2

1 $x = 5, y = 1$ and $x = -3, y = -3$
2 $x = -\frac{2}{5}, y = -\frac{9}{5}$ and $x = 3, y = 5$

42. Direct proportion

(a) $x = 2.4y$ (b) $y = 76.8$ (c) $x = 3.75$

43. Proportionality formulae

1 (a) $v = 3.5z^3$ (b) $v = 20412$
2 (a) $t = 0.92\sqrt{d}$ (b) 5.98 seconds

44. Real-life graphs

(a) 104 km   (b) 45 minutes   (c) 112 km/h

45. Sequences

(a) $3n - 1$ (b) 86   (c) 66
(d) No, 52nd term $= 155$, 53rd term $= 158$

46. Functions

1 (a) $f(1) = 4$ (b) $x = 0$ (c) $b = 1.5$
2 (a) $f(3) = 16$ (b) $f(x) \geqslant 9$ (c) $x < 5$

47. Composite functions

1 (a) $gf(x) = 4x^2 - 8x$ (b) $x = 0, x = 2$
2 (a) $gf(x) = \frac{x + 1}{2x + 1}$ (b) $fg(x) = \frac{3x - 1}{2x - 1}$

48. Inverse functions

1 (a) $f^{-1}(x) = \frac{x + 1}{2}$ (b) 7
2 $g^{-1}(x) = \frac{6}{x - 1}$

49. Functions and graphs

(a) $g(8) = 8$ (b) $fg(12) = 18$ (c) Gradient ≈ -7

50. Differentiation

1 (a) $8x + 6$ (b) $-2x^{-2}$
2 (a) $x^{-2} + x^{-1}$ (b) $-2x^{-3} - x^{-2}$

51. Finding gradients

1 (a) $\frac{dy}{dx} = 9x^2 + 4x$ (b) 44
2 $(0.8, 7.6)$
3 (a) $\frac{dy}{dx} = 6x^2 - 6$
    (b) $(1, -3)$ and $(-1, 5)$

52. Turning points

1 (a) $(4, -13)$
    (b) Minimum, because the coefficient of x^2 is positive
2 (a) $\frac{dy}{dx} = 3x^2 - 10x + 8$
    (b) $x = 2, x = \frac{4}{3}$

53. Kinematics

(a) $\frac{ds}{dt} = 15 - 9.8t$ (b) 10.1 m/s   (c) 11.5 m (1 d.p.)

54-55. Problem-solving practice

1 $t = 4\frac{1}{3}$
2 $C(0, 3), D(-6, 0)$
3 $(7a - 2b)(5a + 4b)$
4 (a) $\frac{x^2 - 2x}{3x^2 - 5x - 2} = \frac{x(x - 2)}{(3x + 1)(x - 2)}$
              $= \frac{x}{3x + 1}$
       $k = 3$
    (b) $f^{-1}(x) = \frac{x}{1 - 3x}$
5 (a) (i) $2x + 3y = 60$
                  $3y = 60 - 2x$
                  $y = 20 - \frac{2}{3}x$
        (ii) $A = xy$
                $= x(20 - \frac{2}{3}x)$
                $= 20x - \frac{2}{3}x^2$
    (b) $\frac{dA}{dx} = 20 - \frac{4}{3}x$
    (c) 150

56. Angle properties

$x = 59°$

57. Solving angle problems

$\angle BDC = x$ (Base angles of an isosceles triangle are equal)
$\angle DBC = 180 - 2x$ (Angles in a triangle add up to 180°)
$\angle ABC = x$ (Base angles of an isosceles triangle are equal)
$\angle ABD = x - (180 - 2x) = 3x - 180$

58. Angles in polygons

15

59. Circle facts

$63.5°$

60. Circle theorems

angle BAC = angle $CBQ = x$ (Alternate segment theorem)
angle $BAD = 180° - 116° = 64°$ (Opposite angles of cyclic
$x + x + 8 = 64$ quad add up to 180°)
    $x = 28°$

61. Intersecting chords

(a) $x = 3.5$ (b) $y = 3.9$ (1 d.p.)

62. Perimeter and area

133 cm²

63. Prisms

Area of cross-section = $\left(15 \times 3 + \frac{1}{2} \times 10 \times 4\right)$ cm^2 = 65 cm^2

Volume of shape = 65 × 8 = 520 cm^3

64. Circles and cylinders

119 cm^2

65. Volumes of 3D shapes

1 $r = 4$ cm

2 Volume box = $\pi \times (3.5)^2 \times 7$

Volume ball = $\frac{4}{3} \times \pi \times (3.5)^3$

Fraction = $\dfrac{4 \times \pi \times (3.5)^3}{3 \times \pi \times (3.5)^2 \times 7} = \dfrac{2}{3}$

66. Pythagoras' theorem

(a) $y = 3.5$ cm (b) $z = 9.1$ cm

67. Pythagoras in 3-D

(a) $TW = 18.4$ cm (1 d.p.)

(b) $WX > YX$ since WX is the hypotenuse of triangle WYX.
In $\triangle TWX$, T rises 7 cm in a horizontal distance of WX.
In $\triangle TYX$, T rises 7 cm in a horizontal distance of YX.
Since $WX > YX$, T rises 7 cm in a shorter distance (YX) in triangle TYX so angle TYX is larger than angle TWX.

68. Surface area

Slant height = $\sqrt{15^2 + 8^2} = 17$

Area cross-section = $\frac{1}{2} \times 16 \times 15 = 120$ cm^2

Area base = $\frac{1}{2} \times \pi \times 8^2 = 100.5309\ldots$ cm^2

Area curved surface = $\frac{1}{2} \times \pi \times 8 \times 17 = 213.6283\ldots$ cm^2

Total surface area = $120 + 100.5309\ldots + 213.6283\ldots$
$= 374.159\ldots = 434$ cm^2 (3 s.f.)

69. Speed

1 4 hours 18 minutes

2 264 miles

70. Converting units

1 111.6 km/h

2 (a) 18 000 cm^2

(b) 42.5 cm^2

(c) 0.84 m^3

71. Similar shapes 1

(a) 130° (b) 31.5 cm

72. Bearings

(a) 225°

(b)

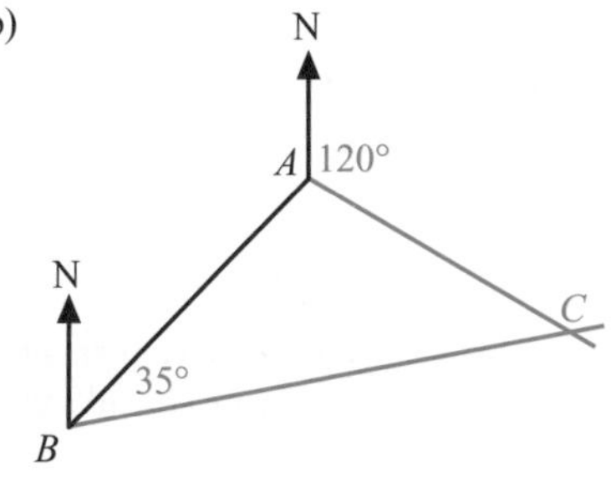

73. Scale drawings and maps

1 9 km

2 1 : 12 500

74. Constructions

1

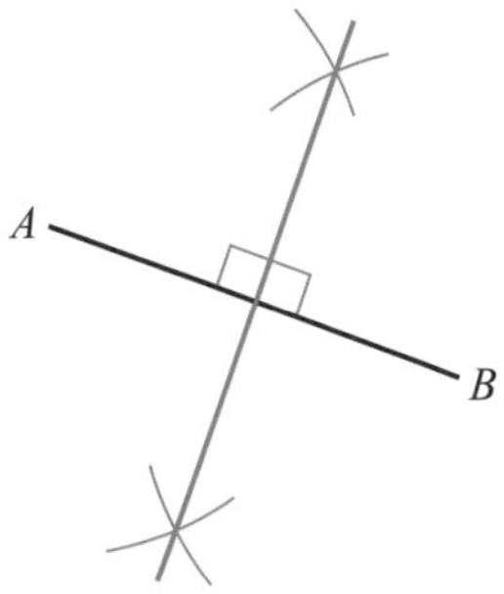

2

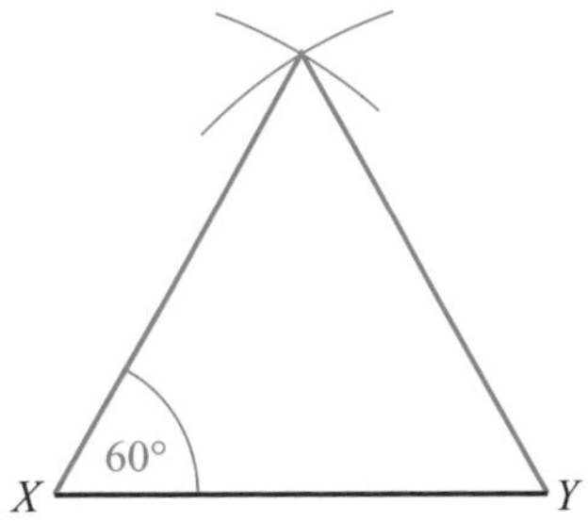

75. Translations, reflections and rotations

(a) Rotation, 90° clockwise, centre (2, 2)

(b) Translation with vector $\begin{pmatrix} -5 \\ -2 \end{pmatrix}$

76. Enlargements

(a), (b)

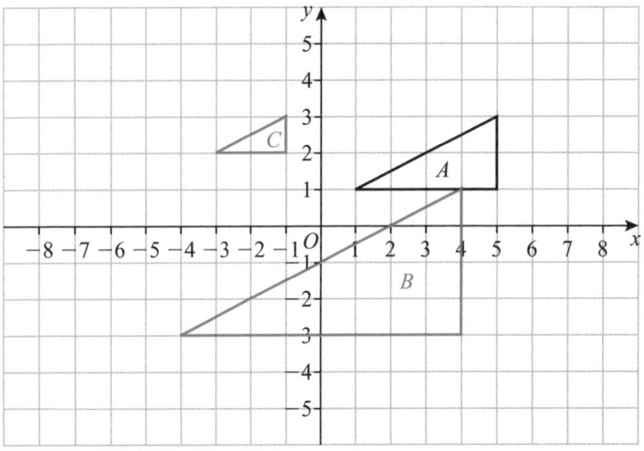

77. Combining transformations

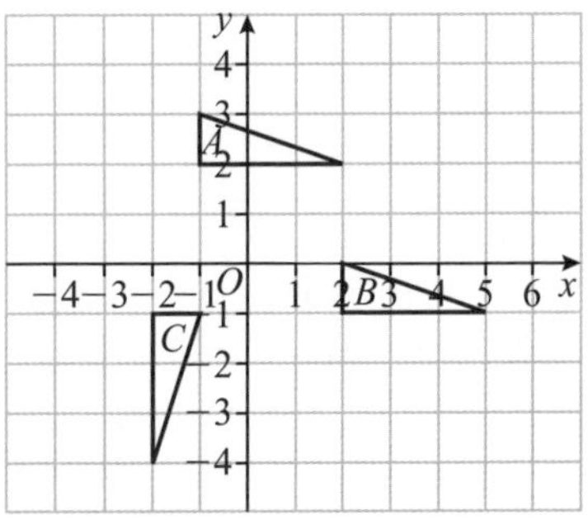

(c) Rotation, 90° anti-clockwise about (−3, 1).

78. Trigonometry 1

(a) 44.8° (b) 56.2° (c) 48.6°

79. Trigonometry 2

(a) 4.4 cm (b) 5.4 cm (c) 15.7 cm

80. The sine rule
(a) 45.2° (3 s.f.)   (b) 15.2 cm (3 s.f.)

81. The cosine rule
Angle PQR = 39.8° (3 s.f.)

82. Trigonometry in 3-D
Angle MJL = 25.0° (3 s.f.)

83. Sectors of circles
Angle AOB = 129°

84. Triangles and segments
Area sector ABC $= \dfrac{135°}{360°} \times \pi \times 4^2 = \dfrac{3}{8} \times \pi \times 16 = 6\pi \text{ cm}^2$

Area $\triangle AOC = \dfrac{1}{2} \times 4 \times 4 \times \sin 135° = \dfrac{8}{\sqrt{2}} = \dfrac{8\sqrt{2}}{2} = 4\sqrt{2} \text{ cm}^2$

Area minor segment ABC = Area sector $-$ area $\triangle$
$\qquad\qquad = 6\pi - 4\sqrt{2} \text{ cm}^2$

85. Similar shapes 2
W = 60 cm X = 765 cm³ Y = 290 cm³ Z = 36 250 cm³

86. Vectors
(a) $2a$
(b) $3b$
(c) $-b + a$
(d) $-2a + 3b$
(e) $\frac{1}{2}a + \frac{9}{4}b$
(f) $\frac{1}{2}a + \frac{1}{4}b$

87. Solving vector problems
(a) $AB = -2\mathbf{a} + 4\mathbf{b}$

$\overrightarrow{HA} = -\mathbf{b} + 2\mathbf{a}$ or $2\mathbf{a} - \mathbf{b}$

$\overrightarrow{JS} = 2\mathbf{b} - \dfrac{2}{3}(-2\mathbf{a} + 4\mathbf{b})$

$\qquad = 2\mathbf{b} + \dfrac{4\mathbf{a}}{3} - \dfrac{8\mathbf{b}}{3} = \dfrac{4\mathbf{a}}{3} - \dfrac{2\mathbf{b}}{3} = \dfrac{2}{3}(2\mathbf{a} - \mathbf{b})$

$\overrightarrow{KT} = \mathbf{b} - \dfrac{1}{3}(-2\mathbf{a} + 4\mathbf{b})$

$\qquad = \mathbf{b} + \dfrac{2\mathbf{a}}{3} - \dfrac{4\mathbf{b}}{3} = \dfrac{2\mathbf{a}}{3} - \dfrac{1\mathbf{b}}{3} = \dfrac{1}{3}(2\mathbf{a} - \mathbf{b})$

$\overrightarrow{HA}$, $\overrightarrow{JS}$ and $\overrightarrow{KT}$ are all multiples of $(2\mathbf{a} - \mathbf{b})$, so are parallel.

(b) $KT : JS : HA$ = 1 : 2 : 3

88-89. Problem-solving practice
1   8 flowerpots
2   5.81 m (3 s.f.)
3   n = 20
4   APB = 30°
5   (a) $a^2 = b^2 + c^2 - 2bc \cos A$
$\qquad 7^2 = x^2 + (x + 5)^2 - 2x(x + 5) \cos 60°$
$\qquad 49 = x^2 + x^2 + 10x + 25 - x^2 - 5x$
$\qquad 49 = x^2 + 5x + 25$
$\qquad 0 = x^2 + 5x - 24$
   (b) x = 3

90. Mean, median and mode
19

91. Frequency table averages
42.25 years

92. Interquartile range
(a) Median = 19 lessons
    Interquartile range = 8 lessons
(b) Students of Instructor A took fewer lessons on average, with a median of 19 compared to 25. The spread of lessons was similar for both instructors, with both having an interquartile range of 8 lessons.

93. Frequency polygons
(a)

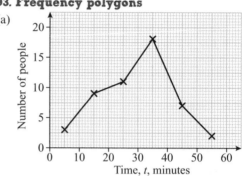

(b) $30 < t \leqslant 40$

94. Histograms
(a)

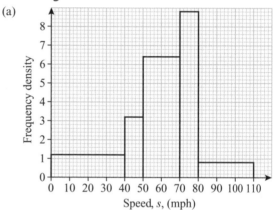

(b) $\dfrac{\left(\frac{128}{4} + 88 + 24\right)}{320} \times 100 = \dfrac{144}{320} \times 100 = 45\%$

95. Cumulative frequency
(a) 29 minutes   (b) 15 minutes   (c) 14%

96. Probability 1
(a) 0.6   (b) 0.9   (c) $0.6 \times 0.6 = 0.36$

97. Probability 2
(a) $420 \times 0.15 + 390 \times 0.2 = 63 + 78 = 141$

(b) $\dfrac{141}{810} = 0.174$

98. Tree diagrams
$\dfrac{70}{132} = \dfrac{35}{66}$

p.99-100 Problem-solving practice
1   x = 11
2   0.33 seconds (2 d.p.)
3   Sunvale farm median = 85 g
    Sunvale farm interquartile range = 11 g
    The weights of the lemons from sunvale farm were greater on average (median of 85 g vs 84 g) but more spread out (interquartile range of 11 g vs 6 g).
4   $\dfrac{3}{30} = \dfrac{1}{10}$
5   P(Correct) $= 0.54 \times 0.8 + 0.31 \times 0.5 + 0.15 \times 0.1 = 0.602$

There are no questions printed on this page.

There are no questions printed on this page.

There are no questions printed on this page.

Published by Pearson Education Limited, Edinburgh Gate, Harlow, Essex, CM20 2JE.

www.pearsonschoolsandfecolleges.co.uk

Copies of official specifications for all Edexcel qualifications may be found on the Edexcel website: www.edexcel.com

Text © Harry Smith and Pearson Education Limited 2014
Edited by Gordon Davies and Linnet Bruce
Typeset and illustrated by Tech-Set Ltd, Gateshead
Original illustrations © Pearson Education Limited 2014
Cover illustration by Miriam Sturdee

The rights of Harry Smith to be identified as author of this work have been asserted by him in accordance with the Copyright,
Designs and Patents Act 1988.

First published 2014

17 16 15 14
10 9 8 7 6 5 4 3 2 1

British Library Cataloguing in Publication Data
A catalogue record for this book is available from the British Library

ISBN 978 0 435 16183 5

Printed in Slovakia by Neografia

Acknowledgements
The publisher would like to thank the following for their kind permission to reproduce their photographs:

(Key: b-bottom; c-centre; l-left; r-right; t-top)

Corbis: Corbis News / John van Hasselt 7

All other images © Pearson Education Limited

Every effort has been made to trace the copyright holders and we apologise in advance for any unintentional omissions. We would be pleased to insert the appropriate acknowledgement in any subsequent edition of this publication

In the writing of this book, no Edexcel examiners authored sections relevant to examination papers for which they have responsibility.